THE
Dementia
Whisperer

SCENES FROM THE FRONTLINE OF CARING

AGNES B. JUHASZ

BOOKS

Hammersmith Health Books

First published in Hungarian in 2014
English language edition first published in 2016 by Hammersmith Health Books –
an imprint of Hammersmith Books Limited
4/4a Bloomsbury Square, London WC1A 2RP, UK
www.hammersmithbooks.co.uk
Reprinted 2016

© 2014, 2016, Agnes B. Juhasz

Note: Whilst the advice and information in this book are believed to be true and
accurate at the date of going to press, neither the author nor the publisher can
accept any legal responsibility or liability for any errors or omissions that may
be made.

Author's note: Sylvia is a fictional person created by the Author as a result
of her experience of caring for numerous people who had different types of
dementia.

British Library Cataloguing in Publication Data: A CIP record of this book is
available from the British Library.

ISBN (print edition): 978-1-78161-096-1
ISBN (ebook): 978-1-78161-097-8

English Language Translation Advisor: Rosie Abensour
Commissioning editor: Georgina Bentliff
Edited by: Ruth Atkinson
Cover design and typesetting by: Sylvia Kwan
Production: Helen Whitehorn, Path Projects Ltd
Printed and bound by: TJ International Ltd of Padstow, Cornwall, UK

CONTENTS

INTRODUCTION

My school and college years were pure fun rather than being the basis of my future profession. I had no idea that years later I would be so passionate about being a healthcare professional. Back then, I always used to say: 'I'll never work in healthcare, not even for 24 hours.' This attitude made me very popular among my classmates and I kept my promise for over a decade after leaving school, more or less, as my interests moved towards very different areas where I was given the opportunity to express myself through journalistic work, which I really enjoyed.

All this changed fundamentally when I decided to move from my home in Hungary to Australia. There is a huge need for nurses in the land of kangaroos, so it seemed to be a good idea to sign up for a nursing course. I got my Diploma and became an Endorsed Enrolled Nurse (EEN) two years later. I had no worries about employment with this profession as there were plenty of jobs available and Australian society has a very high respect for, and public appreciation of, nurses. Not to mention the practical side of it – as a foreigner my Diploma offered the benefit of always being taken favourably into account when it came to my visa renewals.

What had started for practical reasons suddenly became a passion when I started my first job in a dementia-specific programme and became a practitioner of very special care work. Before my training as a nurse I had never heard of dementia – that specific group of symptoms caused by damage to the brain, the most common type of which is Alzheimer's syndrome.

I was lucky enough to have employers who emphasised the importance of ongoing training and education, so I was sent to attend national and international conferences, workshops and exhibitions, where the best presenters and professionals shared their ideas and the latest results of research on this topic. I started at the most basic level and went through all the steps in dementia care, something I am very grateful for, as you cannot achieve a truly thorough understanding and detailed knowledge of the intriguing world of this disease without this comprehensive training.

I first worked with people living with dementia in 2007. Since then I have been walking through the maze of the condition with increasing confidence, leading by the hand those who are lost in it; those who are no longer able to turn the next corner without help. They are confused, apprehensive, frustrated, sad and lonely.

In the blink of an eye I was pulled deep into the labyrinth of the disease. Without my making any effort, all the pieces of specific information that I had gained at college and conferences, and my own personal experiences, suddenly just fell into place as if the maze's map was revealed in an instant. From then on, I was seduced by the hidden secrets and endless wonder that make up dementia. A vocation had been born.

My insight into the world of this condition began with my job as a carer at an overnight respite home for culturally and linguistically diverse people who were living with dementia. As my shifts were always changing, I had a great opportunity to see the differences in behaviour and daily routine of the people in my care throughout the whole 24-hour period.

Several years later, I was lucky enough to become the coordinator of this same dementia-specific programme. This offered me a wider view and gave me a further perspective on the disease – other than that of a carer or a person with dementia – as I came to know all the main organisations, government departments, decision makers, funding agencies and service providers who had their own say in this national health priority. As well as having the responsibility for providing appropriate training for the staff, and writing and submitting funding applications, one of my main roles was to assess and then draw up a care plan for every individual who entered the respite home.

I visited affected families and assessed what the needs of the people with dementia would be during their stay at the facility. Everybody was involved in these conversations and I always made sure that I delved as deeply as possible in order to find the person behind the condition. Several of the people who stayed at the respite home had very limited spoken English, either because they had never learnt it or because, due to their condition, they had forgotten every other language but their mother tongue. This was quite a challenge, especially in relation to dementia, where a wide range of communication techniques is used to help the person understand and be understood. As a result of learning about these people's life stories, their cultures and traditions, I adopted different routines into person-centred care plans for people with dementia from countless different countries, including Croatia, Greece, Hungary, India, Indonesia, Italy, Portugal, Romania, Russia, Samoa, Serbia and Spain.

As the leader of the programme, it was extremely important to me to have daily personal contact with those staying at the home. I insisted on being on call most of the time and was happy to answer emergency calls if a staff member on duty could not cope with a sudden behaviour change or with aggression, confident that, drawing on experience built up over the years, I could resolve the most extreme situations and cope with very challenging behaviour that many people would be tempted to give up on.

In 2012, my knowledge and experience in dementia care were further extended when I started to work as a live-in carer in the UK.

I have therefore had the remarkable opportunity to study the world of dementia and observe people with the condition throughout the day, for days, weeks, months, and in one particular case, years, at a time. From early morning until late at night, and often in the middle of the night, I have shared the lives of those with dementia. I have seen different types and symptoms of the disease, as well as deterioration or temporary improvements in the condition. It is an indescribable feeling and a unique experience that you could never learn as part of a course.

■ ■ ■

This book draws on my experience in dementia care in Australia and the UK. Both countries take this care very seriously: ageing populations mean that more and more people are involved in this mental condition as the number affected increases; they are involved either as patients, carers, family members, neighbours or friends. My aim is to guide readers gently through the amazing maze of the world of dementia in order to provide support and hope to all those affected by the disease.

At the same time, I would like to emphasise that I am neither a doctor nor a scientist. Far from using medical terminology to introduce and explain the condition, I have used straightforward everyday terms, practical experience and real-life stories to provide information about the disease, using examples to illustrate the typical symptoms of different stages and the most bewildering behaviours of dementia. In doing so I rely on facts rather than hearsay and myths.

It is my hope that, when the reader emerges from the labyrinth at the end of the book, although it is an irreversible and incurable condition, dementia will appear much less frightening than originally thought. My goal is to clear up the confusion in people's minds about the subject and to answer questions, such as: 'What are the differences between the main different types of dementia?' 'Can dementia be prevented?' 'Can or should the process of dementia be slowed down?' 'What predictable changes will a person diagnosed with dementia experience?' 'Can a person with the disease live happily and with a good quality of life?' 'How can the quality of life of a person living with the condition be improved?'

It is important to make it clear at the beginning that there are as many different practices and techniques for caring for people with dementia as there are individuals, because all interactions are built on a person-centred approach based on the person's life history, habits and personality. Actions and reactions grow out of this, and carers draw from that basic knowledge when faced with challenging behaviour changes.

Nevertheless, there are certain universal methods and 'golden rules' when it comes to the disease. Using these tools, miracles can be achieved and obstacles that come sometimes by the dozen can be conquered effectively. Going to bed with a clear conscience is hard to achieve in dementia care, but it is definitely not impossible.

I cannot even begin to approximate how many people with dementia I have met and how many life stories I have known. These people and their condition have taken me on a fascinating journey and, consequently, I have learnt something very deep about myself that has changed my life forever. I thank the wonderful people I have cared for all around the globe for this story. It was they who let me step into their incredible and distorted world where we have walked hand in hand through the invisible labyrinth which confronts anyone who has to face the challenges dementia brings. It is into this maze that I now invite you, the reader.

CHAPTER
1

TIGHTROPE WALKING
ON MY NERVES

I am counting the seconds. All I want is to stretch time out and make my break a bit longer before she returns home. I wander about the house restlessly, looking out of the window, waiting for the source of my stress to return. Nothing and no one. Then the car stops outside. Immediately I go to my bedroom, because this is the room that is furthest away from the front door and the only place in the house where I can bear the sharp sound of the bell. Bimm-bamm, bimm-bamm. Always twice! I have no idea why she is so obsessed by it, but she always has to press it twice before entering the house.

Jeanne is standing at the door, smiling. With one hand she is helping Sylvia to step inside, while with the other hand she passes the wallet and the parking permit back to me. Sylvia is surprised that somebody is home, just as she is every single time that she comes back to the house and finds me there, but she sits cooperatively on the little stool in the hall to change her shoes to her more comfortable indoor pair. We all move into the living room. Jeanne starts writing up her documentation and

I make sure that Sylvia is settled in her favourite spot on the sofa where we can have our usual 'welcome back' conversation.

'So, where have you been today?' I ask.

The question is unfair of course, as I know exactly where she has spent her time this afternoon. I checked the receipt as soon as Jeanne gave me the wallet, so I know that she was taken to George's Farm.

'We went to the Lily Garden,' she says automatically, as she does every time she has to answer this question.

Jeanne and I quickly glance at each other, and we both know that we can skip the topic. My beloved lady does not have the faintest idea where she has been for two hours, but that is fine.

Sylvia has dementia. She is in her nineties and is a fragile, sweet, lovable old woman whom everybody wants to hug, support and mollycoddle at first sight, just as they would an adorable toddler, which is exactly how I felt the first time I saw her.

I clearly remember the morning when I was looking out at the wing of the plane through the window; the ground staff were de-icing it with steam in preparation for take-off. 'Oh please, let it be able to take off. I do not want to be stuck in Hungary,' I thought. It was snowing hard outside. My plane was full of Hungarians and most of them, like me, were coming to work in England. However, my original plan had been something totally different. I had planned to go back to Hungary and live and work there.

It all started when, after three years of being away from my homeland, I finally managed to time a return visit home from Australia to coincide with Christmas. It was a big mistake, but I could not help it; I really missed a snowy, white, real Christmas after those years of celebrating the festival in 40 degrees, wearing shorts and having BBQs in my backyard. One month after returning to Australia in the New Year, I realised I wanted to move back to the 'old continent'. I suppose I had experienced a sort of reverse culture shock during my Christmas holiday at home, and, just like an awakening, it became crystal clear to me that I am a European and will be forever. It is something I cannot change. From that moment on, I spent my time arranging my permanent homecoming, which I eventually achieved 18 months later. After the years I had spent in Australia, I was truly surprised how easy it was to get a job in the EU in terms of a work permit and paperwork. But when my plan came to fruition and I finally I got what I wanted – I was back in Hungary – I very soon had to confront the fact that my home is different now and things have changed. People say that if you have been away for a long time, you do not belong to either the new or the old country any more and there is truth in that saying. I decided to accept the offer of a job in England.

My plane did finally take off, and I started a brand new chapter of my life, a remarkable journey exploring every little puddle, tree, stream, field, forest and lake of the land of this smiling-crying sort of mental condition called dementia. Sylvia is my travel guide, even if she does not know it.

When I first met her, on a cold, winter day in early February, I was relieved. Although I had been given advance information about her, it is always a matter of chance whether a carer and the person with dementia will get on together.

Having had four years' experience of working in the field of dementia, I had specifically requested work with someone living with this disease, because not everybody likes doing this kind of care work. In my view, it does have its sunny moments, although there is no denying it has plenty of shadows as well. I knew Sylvia was considerably affected by dementia, but had been told that her condition was bearable.

Sylvia was sitting at the kitchen table with her back to the front door when I stepped into her life. While I was getting the snow off my boots by gently tapping my feet on the doormat, I kept an eye on her and observed that the lady in the kitchen was very elegant, smart looking and well groomed, but unbelievably small and frail. I went into the kitchen, introduced myself politely, calling her by her surname, and she reciprocated my good manners by asking me to call her Sylvia. As soon as we had got through the introductions, I mentally put aside the official care plan, and started building a unique profile based on my own observations.

My baseline, of course, remained the one provided by the care company, but that contained only very basic information. These profiles are mostly facts about the condition, medication, family members, contact numbers, dietary needs and warnings, together with a very brief life history. This information was a good start, but I still had to find my way to a so far unknown personality, with an absolutely unique life. Finding out more would be determined by whether or not she wanted to talk about herself.

To create a complete profile, you need much more than bare facts. It requires constant observation, intuition and understanding, as well as a recording and analysis of different situations, possible conflicts and incidents, in order to develop and adapt helping strategies. These eventually provide a useful guide and a more accurate map in the wonderland of a broken mind.

I had never worked with people with dementia as a live-in carer before. What I have since realised is that the 24/7 constant work gives me a great opportunity to fathom the unknown depths of the disease as I am literally living my everyday life with someone whose condition makes every single day a new challenge for her, turning her reality upside down as it does mine too.

Apart from sleeping time – although that too is often disturbed by an unexpected event – I spend every moment with Sylvia. I watch her, listen to her, talk to her and support her behaviour and life by metaphorically holding her hand and guiding her through the possible obstacles and difficulties of the day. At the same time, I respect her independence and encourage her to do things for herself as much as possible within her physical limits, even if it takes a hundred times more energy out of me than simply doing it for her.

I do all this automatically now. But I have to admit that at first I was taken aback by her symptoms. In the initial phase of getting to know each other, I soon found out that, unlike some people with dementia, she could talk very fluently, but I was disconcerted by the way she would suddenly switch the topic and, without any warning, start to talk about her parents, consistently using the present tense.

I listen wide-eyed to her story, actively nodding and giving her my complete attention.

'Mama is on stage tonight and Papa has been travelling somewhere.'

I am careful with what my facial expression betrays on hearing this astonishing news and I am especially cautious about not correcting her, so she continues.

'I wish we could find a matinee show as I would like to take you to see Mama on stage. She's a wonderful actress.'

I do not check in the files, I just do the sums in my head. Sylvia is in her nineties so her parents cannot possibly still be alive. What can I do? More importantly, what can I say?

I am not supposed to lie. Although I know what a comfort it is for people with dementia to drift back to the past, into a particular, precise moment when they were happy and unworried, when they experienced most of the positive experiences of their life, I cannot go with her into this train of thought and confirm her delusion.

Diversion is the only fair option I have at my disposal to avoid our conversation becoming completely bizarre.

'What did you used to do for a living?' I ask, hoping that the topic will divert her from Mama and the stage.

'Actually, my dear, I am supposed to be at the factory right now, but I have decided not to go in for a few days to see how they get on without me.'

'Hmmm,' I think to myself. I realise that being with Sylvia is not going to be the easiest task in my life.

People with dementia usually have strong memories from the first 25 years of their lives because this part – childhood and young adulthood – is the most significant, with positive memories such as family celebrations, school years, a first job, love or marriage. Music therapists working with people living with the condition always focus on melodies that were popular from this period. By listening to these tunes, people with the disease are able to recall pleasant experiences that make them feel safe and happy again. The music leads them, as it were, back to their comfort zone.

Sylvia's comfort zone is definitely rooted in her time as a child and as a young adult with her parents, and I have to resort to the art of diversion several times a day. She has built an especially strong 'brick wall of memories' from this era around her still-functioning brain areas:

the faces, names and situations from her first quarter century are still there and mean reality for her. She therefore lives her everyday life in a maze built around these flashbacks. There are a few clues at the turning points and crossroads that help her to turn right or left, but there are no exit signs: fundamentally, she will never get out of this labyrinth again.

Short-term memory – the ability to remember whether or not they have had lunch, where they put the tweezers that they used only five minutes ago – no longer functions in a person living with dementia. The level of malfunction of the brain areas that are responsible for short-term memory storage in these people depends on many things, mainly the type and the stage of the disease. The daily signs of Sylvia's advanced level of short-term memory loss give me the toughest and greatest challenges to my patience and creativity that I have ever experienced.

To help identify the extent of the problem, one morning I decided to make a list of how many times and what type of things she would repeat both verbally and in her actions at the beginning of the day.

Like a real acrobat, Sylvia starts the first act of her tightrope walking on my nerves as she prepares to clean her teeth. I gently suggest that toothpaste would be more efficient than the facial scrub she is about to put on her toothbrush. When she has finished, I have to reassure her four times that she has brushed her teeth.

We move on to breakfast in the kitchen. I try to use the same script every day as consistency and predictability are the best friends of someone living with dementia; they certainly help to keep the chronic anxiety under control. But we still have numerous repetitions. After sitting down to her cornflakes, Sylvia asks me three times if I will sit down too.

I automatically answer questions that are always the same and always come on cue as I carry on making my breakfast.

After breakfast is over we go six times through the topic of when we are going to have breakfast. I explain over and over again that we have just had it.

'But if you are hungry, I am happy to make something else for you,' I finally concede.

'Oh no, goodness gracious, I am so full. Thank you, sweetie,' she says.

A few seconds later, the next repeat question cuts into my nearly settled mind. 'Darling, can you tell me when exactly are you planning for us to have breakfast?' And we start the whole conversation from the beginning again, which takes quite a while. I recognise that this is a part of our morning routine.

Finally, we move into the living room and start to watch Sylvia's favourite TV shows. The stories do not make much sense to her any more, but they provide a gentle, familiar background noise rather than anything else.

It was clear right from the start that if I am cross, Sylvia will be doubly cross. Like a reflection in the mirror, people with dementia copy behaviour and body language, and on top of that, they are extremely sensitive to every little mood change. But with some adaptive skills it is possible to overcome the madness that can easily overcome the carer when looking after someone living with this type of advanced mental disorder.

I must admit that there were occasions and days in the first few weeks when I took very mild over-the-counter tranquillisers in order to deal with the extreme tension I felt, but gradually I developed the skill to be able to follow a story on TV while actively participating in a conversation, either verbally or with gestures.

It took time to get to this point, but it has become one of my survival tools and now I use this technique automatically. I can be watching and listening to the news while Sylvia keeps talking about the things that weigh on her mind.

'Mama is so short, but it's incredible how she is transformed on the stage into someone tall and glamorous. If my son comes, you must ask him to tell us the date of the next matinee show, then you can see for yourself.'

'Of course, I will talk to him,' I say, and at the same time I take in the petrol price rise and my mind is engaged in an interesting discussion of economics in the TV studio that I am watching on the big screen. I even nod and smile when necessary and give my standard answers when the right moment comes. This seeming participation makes Sylvia feel comfortable and safe and encourages her to keep talking.

We can do this for hours, sustained by tea and biscuits. I keep saying my usual 'yes', 'of course', 'I see' or 'I agree', and she knows I am there. Naturally, if it comes to something real and specific that she says or wants to talk about in the present, unrelated to the 'thousand-times-repeated-stories', my listening changes immediately and I focus on her, and only her.

■ ■ ■

Orientation in time and place is one of the most significant tasks of a carer for people with dementia as they can be very confused and constantly need someone to tell them 'when', 'where' and 'how long'. A clear calendar helps, and although this is less effective in the advanced stages of the disease, one of the fundamental principles of care work of this kind is the 'I'm still here' approach.[1]

Even though it sometimes seems pointless to keep a habit or a routine going, people living with this condition have a right to continue doing what they used to do and used to enjoy. Although the way they see the world now is filtered as a result of a disease which sometimes distorts reality, they still have the right to as good a quality of life as possible, and the right to express themselves in a way that gives them joy and pleasure. Freedom of choice is as important to people with dementia as it is to anybody else. They may not understand the meaning of the choices they are being given, but they are certainly aware of how they are being treated, and how life can be easier and more enjoyable. Even in a condition which affects both physical and mental health, life and the way a person feels can be well balanced so that less inner stress or tension and less conflict from the outside world are experienced.

The habits and routines retained will naturally vary according to the individual. This is where the family can help a lot by sharing important information regarding the hobbies of the people being cared for, what they were really interested in before the disease arrived, what kind of music they used to like, what types of things they used to do for leisure.

Following the 'I'm still here' approach, even if a person with dementia no longer reads the whole of a favourite newspaper or magazine any more, or does not even understand a single article in it, just holding or looking through the familiar paper or journal gives pleasure. Showing favourite films again and again also conjures up pleasant memories from the time before the disease took hold.

The first mistake one can make as a carer is generalisation. Just because somebody is old, it does not necessarily mean that they like to play Bingo, have a nap in the afternoon or eat custard creams. In fact, these things may really annoy them. A completely person-centred approach must be used when dealing with dementia in order to find the human being behind the mental state. It is no good just looking at the disease or the age of the person, the carer must see who they really are. People living with the condition have the absolute right not to be treated like idiots. Rather than being classified as 'forever mad', they have the right to live a full life, within their own horizons.

■ ■ ■

My worst days are the ones when Sylvia expects visitors – a family member, a friend or a service provider – or something is due to happen that changes our well-established routine. These days are worse because Sylvia steps out of her comfort zone and gets overexcited about the event to come. Remembering the 'I'm still here' principle, the principles of respect and of treating a person with dignity, I tell Sylvia every single morning what day, month and year it is and talk through what is happening in the next 24 hours, including any visitors or appointments.

Each day is about constant preparation for the events ahead, more or less, whether the event is an everyday routine, like lunch, or something out of the usual routine. One particular day when we were expecting the chiropodist at 6 p.m. stands out in my mind. Sylvia started getting ready for his visit from the moment I first mentioned the appointment.

'What time are we having lunch?' Sylvia asks.

'At twelve thirty, like every day.'

'Oh I hope everything is going to be all right by the time Nick arrives. I don't want the house to smell of food.'

'Don't worry, we'll have plenty of time before he comes at six. I'll open the windows to get rid of the smell after lunch; is that all right?'

'Don't be silly. That won't be necessary. Why didn't you say *before that he's only coming at six? Such a relief!' She sighs.*

Barely thirty seconds pass before our next conversation.

'You know what, sweetie, I think we should have lunch a bit earlier today, because I don't want the house to smell of food when the chiropodist arrives.'

'He won't come before six, I'm one hundred per cent sure about that,' I reply and am surprised how calm my voice sounds.

'Oh, silly me. You see I was worrying about nothing. It's all right then, we have plenty of time till he comes,' she smiles.

'That's true. No worries; everything will be absolutely ready by then.'

'Did you get the basin and the towel ready? We are going to need them and he will be here any minute now,' she says one minute after our previous discussion. It is still only ten o'clock. 'Just how long is this day going to last?' I ask myself.

Sylvia takes the basin and towel out of the cupboard. She carefully folds the towel and in the same accurate way she places the basin with the towel beside it on the sofa in the living room.

Then she repeatedly asks me about the time and whether the chiropodist is late. I answer over and over again that he's not coming until six.

She eventually looks at her watch and nearly shouts from surprise and relief when she sees the actual time: 'Oh dear, we've got plenty of time! Why didn't you say anything when you saw me putting these things out? They'll be dusty by then. You should have said it was too early for all this preparation.' Of course it is my fault.

Sylvia carefully puts the towel and basin back in the

cupboard and sits down in her armchair, where she starts to check the contents of her handbag. I decide to sneak away for a short break in my room.

When I come into the living room just a few minutes later I see that the basin and the towel are out again and are quizzing me from the same spot as before, in the middle of the sofa. I say nothing. There is no point. I remind myself that I am a guest, if not an intruder, in Sylvia's house. I must follow the golden rule that, whatever the mental state of people with dementia, they can do anything freely as long as it is safe for them and for others.

Between the time when I first mention the appointment and ten minutes before the appointment time, Sylvia puts the basin and the towel in and out of the cupboard a total of forty-two times.

We are both restless and keep walking around the house. Sylvia is the leader. I just follow in her footsteps and without her noticing put back all the objects that she moves for some reason into really odd places, perhaps guided by confusion, anxiety or some irrational idea. I find the kitchen towel on the bookshelf, a spoon on top of the piano, a piece of bread in the armchair. Maybe moving objects helps her to let off steam while we are waiting.

She keeps checking and rechecking everything. Sylvia makes me promise again and again that I will offer Nick coffee or tea as soon as he arrives and is continually anxious that we have not got enough money to pay him. I keep showing her the cash that we have got ready. Neither of us doubts the right of the basin and the towel to be on the sofa any more. We agree that they have to be there and that it is time to show them off,

19

though for the record, Nick never uses them as he brings his own equipment.

There are only a few minutes to go and Sylvia comes into the living room following her latest wandering. She suddenly notices the objects on the sofa: the red basin and the matching towel with the flower pattern. She hesitates for a second, then turns towards me and asks: 'How strange, do you know what these things are doing here?'

She really means it.

'The chiropodist will be here any minute now; they are ready for him,' I reply. I am just about to say something else in my calmest ever voice when her next comment means that, despite all my training, I cannot contain my amusement.

'I had no idea that you're having your feet done today.'

After all the day-long hassle about the pedicure, being able to smile again is so refreshing, like a natural medicine to my tired mind.

CHAPTER
2

PERSONAL INSULTS

The biggest challenge in caring for someone living with dementia is that the most common symptom for those fighting the disease is forgetfulness, whereas those caring for that person remember. Week by week carers build up a backlog of bad memories that poison their minds, but which the other party cannot recall even two minutes after they happened.

Although Sylvia does her best, she has an incredible talent for turning the day into a nightmare if she is in the mood to do so. She has a very complex personality and exercises my creativity and patience time and time again. She has a great sense of humour, which helps a lot, but she has her own very clear ideas about what is good for her.

I was curious to know whether Sylvia has always been like this or whether this is part of her condition, so I checked by asking her daughter. Apparently Sylvia has always been stubborn and rather hot-headed, so her dementia has only highlighted these already existing personal characteristics. Sometimes it is possible for a person affected by this chronic mental condition to experience a total change of personality and behaviour, though how negatively is very variable, but this was not the case with Sylvia.

I never cease to be amazed by the memories dementia leaves intact and those it decides to take away forever. For example, I find it fascinating that Sylvia's make-up routine seems to be hardwired and that she continues to care about her appearance in her nineties. It is wonderful how a personality still manages to shine through even with this brain-devouring disease. Sylvia does not remember whether or not she ate five minutes ago, yet she always remembers to put her make-up on before she leaves her bedroom. However, there are problems with putting her make-up routine into practice as her judgement, as well as the coordination of certain movements, is considerably impaired in the advanced stage of the condition.

I never know whether to laugh or cry on the very few mornings when she wakes up earlier than me and tries to cope with all the hassle of getting dressed and made up on her own. She is bored, so she is not going to wait for me and prefers to keep herself busy by putting on every single piece of clothing she can lay her hands on – a feat that, for her, equals the achievement of running an Olympic marathon. The result is sometimes disastrous, as it was the other day when she answered my quiet knock on her door and permitted me to enter her room.

As soon as I open the door I am knocked out by the bad odour caused by the fuggy smell of urine somewhere in the room. Unfortunately accidents do happen, whether or not pads are worn. But what is even more grotesque is the scene which meets my eyes.

Sylvia is sitting on the chair beside the window, still wearing her nightdress. Her bra is inside out and upside down over the top of her nightdress in such a way that it is hanging on her in a most awkward position, mocking her femininity and dignity.

Literally everything, the whole of her body from top to toe and everything she is wearing, is covered in face powder, not dusted on lightly and smoothly, but applied in thick, caked patches. Abstract lines of vivid-coloured lipstick stand out on her face on and all around her lovely lips. It is such a bizarre sight I find it very hard not to laugh, but I must not let my amusement show. She is smiling at me and it is clear she believes she looks pretty good: her ladyship is ready for the day. She is not aware that she has just drawn her own caricature and that I am going to wash it away in a few minutes, along with the unpleasant smell, under the shower.

Sylvia's stubbornness and determination in wanting to start the day dressed and made up are astounding, and if the only result is extra work for me, there is absolutely no harm in her being allowed to do as she wants. However, it is sometimes more difficult for a carer to rise above hurtful remarks, and continual fault-finding can be very wearing.

My coffee making went all to pieces because of Sylvia's constant criticism. No matter how hard I tried to please her, I just could not make the coffee right. It was not even the type of coffee made from fresh coffee beans that connoisseurs prefer and praise; it was only ordinary instant coffee made with hot water and milk – Sylvia did not like sugar in her coffee. I kept trying to work out what I had failed to do.

I feel like an idiot. Every single time I make a coffee for Sylvia, she criticises it after the first sip. In her view, it is not even drinkable.

'The milk has gone off! Yuck, there is no way I can drink this! It's a nightmare,' she exclaims.

'It can't be off. I only bought it this morning when I went shopping.'

She has another sip, her face clearly showing her disgust. It is clear she is not going to give up on her criticism.

When she has drunk nearly the whole cup, the criticism starts again, as if she has been thinking all the time how she can make her distaste clear.

'Something is still not right with this coffee. I am sure it is the milk.'

She stands up, walks to the kitchen sink and pours all the coffee left in the cup down the drain. I feel hurt, of course, but I say nothing. After all, I cannot shout into her face what I am really thinking: that she is totally confused and only pleased when she can criticise something or somebody.

I kept thinking about my coffee making and wondered if there was something else that was bothering her that made her so rebellious when it came to her morning cup of coffee. Perhaps she was only letting off steam and the coffee was not the actual cause. But I got nowhere. Coffee time became a recurring problem for both of us.

I poured my heart into making Sylvia's coffee and I was convinced it was delicious, but all my efforts were useless. Despite all my endeavours, the coffee I made was pronounced unsatisfactory day after day. It was 'too hot', 'tasted peculiar' or 'not hot enough'. It had 'too much milk' or 'too much coffee' in it. I could not bear the relentless criticism any longer. I was just about to give up. It was grinding me down. I realised I had to do something about the situation.

I decided to change tactics and have my response ready for when Sylvia next asked for a coffee.

'Could you please make it? You know how clumsy I am when it comes to coffee making. Besides, I know you make the best coffee ever, and just the way you like it.'

She is willing to teach me how to do it, so she invites me to stand by the kettle with the cup ready next to it and the demonstration starts. The way she makes the coffee is identical to the way I have always tried to make the best possible instant coffee. However, I pretend that I am fascinated by the way she does it and she enjoys her role as demonstrator very much.

'You see, gorgeous,' I say, 'That is why I will never make coffee in this house again. I could never do what you have just done, no matter how hard I try.'

She sniffs out the trap. 'Sweetie, I have never criticised your way of making coffee!'

The conversation ends there, but silently I just add a few words to it in my head. I cannot help it: it is good for my soul! Yet it is what happens next that makes me feel even better. She pulls a face as soon as she takes her first sip.

'There is something wrong with this coffee. I am sure it is the milk,' she bristles at it.

The next time I make coffee I decide to try a different approach and have my response to her first critical remark at the ready.

'This coffee is undrinkable!' Sylvia exclaims.

Instead of trying to persuade her that everything is all right and that the coffee tastes good, I say: 'Yes, I've noticed on my cup that the coffee leaves a really nasty ring. Look. It looks horrible.'

'Oh yes, there's one on mine too. Unbelievable!' she responds.

'Next time I go to the local shop, I'll talk to the shopkeeper and ask him to suggest a different brand, because this is definitely not the best.'

'You must tell them that you are buying it for me; everybody knows me there. Then you'll be sure you're getting the best,' she advises.

I nod while I continue with my little experiment, trying to provide some fixed points for her twisted reality.

'To be honest, I can't say it tastes bad, because it doesn't, but if you want, I can throw this out. You don't have to drink it if you don't like it.'

'No thank you, sweetie, I'd rather drink it. I didn't say it was undrinkable.'

She drinks another mouthful.

'Ugh! The milk must be out of date!'

I realise that, in acknowledging the fact that the coffee was not good, I had only temporarily turned off Sylvia's criticism.

The shopkeeper is very helpful when I spell out the situation and I return from my next grocery shop with a new brand of instant coffee. I show Sylvia the jar, explain that I have bought a much better brand of coffee following the shopkeeper's recommendation and that, if she wants, I can throw the old jar out now. She is very surprised.

'My goodness me, no. I hate wasting food or drink. We should finish the old one first, then we can try this new brand.'
I make the coffee and the criticism starts all over again.
Finally, the light goes on in my head and I understand. The criticism is a compulsory part of the game, part of her drinking her coffee. The same scene has to be played out every single time Sylvia has coffee, no matter how it is made and no matter who makes it.

I get plenty of criticism and negative comments from Sylvia throughout the day, but step by step I have learnt how not to take them personally. No matter what the person with dementia says, and no matter what the circumstances, not taking things personally is a fundamental principle in the endless and very complex process of dementia care.

Carers can be brought to tears by people with this condition making nasty comments or calling them names. It is a natural human reaction, but it does not help for two reasons. Firstly, it does nothing at all to help a carer get out of a challenging situation and deal with the problem. Crying can upset the person with dementia even more, making them more confused, more agitated and less cooperative. Secondly, people with the disease do not remember five minutes later if they have said anything hurtful as it is just an instinctive reaction for them. When they use unkind and unpleasant words, it is usually only to express some physical or emotional discomfort.

By avoiding crying and self-pity, a carer's response can be more effective if he or she applies certain practical techniques. Simply ignoring the verbal attack, pretending that everything is as per normal and showing no reaction to the bad language, is an excellent way to settle a person with dementia. Using this strategy along with diversion works very well in the majority of cases. At the same time, carers should get their 'processors' working and watch out for those things that trigger agitation, mood swings and significant changes in behaviour.

Sylvia is diabetic, so her blood sugar levels can change drastically. One particular day, when I left too much time between meals, turned into a real ordeal.

It is eleven in the morning and Sylvia is starting to behave very oddly. She is picking a quarrel over everything, looking for objects that she has to move to another place, anxiously searching for things that she never usually wants or uses. Now she is picking on the candles. The candles are not where they are supposed to be kept and this is a huge problem. I take her to the cabinet in the living room where she always keeps them as I am confident that finding them there will calm her down, but I am totally wrong! She flies into a tantrum and becomes very aggressive.

'Who was the foolish idiot who put them here? I would never use this cabinet to store them. The candles do not belong in here!'

She grabs the plastic bag, hesitates for a few seconds, then suddenly makes her way to the cupboard in the hall and places them on the top shelf. I keep a careful eye on what she is doing, otherwise we will never find the candles again. She certainly will not remember where she has put them, that is for sure.

Ever since the sudden change in her behaviour started, I have been thinking hard about the possible cause and the diagnosis comes to me in a flash. She must be hungry. She had breakfast early and refused to have anything to eat with her morning coffee.

Although a routine is important in this type of care work, so is flexibility. I hurry into the kitchen and start to prepare everything I will need for cooking lunch earlier than usual.

I can still hear that Sylvia is in a rage because of the candles, swearing and calling the unknown person who moved her beloved candles from one place to another by all sorts of names: in this case I have escaped direct blame.

She keeps shuffling back and forth between the cupboard and the cabinet in the living room, constantly shaking the plastic bag in her hand. I know she will keep doing this until lunch is ready. Trying to convince her that the place where we found the candles is where she has always kept them would be just like adding fuel to the fire.

Instead I speed up the cooking, arrange the lunch decoratively on her plate and invite her to sit down to a delicious-smelling and tempting-looking meal of breaded fish and vegetable rice. It is only when she sits down at the table that she finally puts down the bagful of candles.

My hunch was right. She needs to eat. The candles are not mentioned any more for the rest of the day.

In the case of the candles, low blood sugar levels were the main cause, but it is not always possible with Sylvia to identify a reason for what she has done, is doing or is likely to do. Sometimes it seems that she just does things because she is in a contrary mood. This can cause trouble as well as some amusing moments.

The freshly made food I place in front of her at mealtimes often comes in for a barrage of criticism. My personal favourite, when she can think of no alternative to her usual remarks, such as 'too salty', 'too much pepper', 'too chewy' or 'too cold', is when she simply says 'too boring'. In my experience, it is very important always to make the food look attractive and to serve a variety of food, so I am stumped when it comes to a suitable reply to that remark!

On one of the occasions when 'boring' had been the verdict, I offered Sylvia the salt, suggesting that it might make her meal more interesting.

Sylvia gratefully accepts the salt. She never lets me or others salt her food as she believes it is a task that she is still perfectly capable of doing.

I would not even think of trying to take the illusion of independence away from her, but behind my straight-faced expression, I carefully check her actions. I can see that she is putting too much salt on her plate, so I quickly think of an indirect way of warning her that will not be too humiliating.

As though the thought has just come into my mind, I comment: 'People say that we have to be careful about using too much salt in our food if we want to live a long and healthy life.'

She keeps on adding salt.

I am not going to give up.

'What about if we try the food as it is? Then we can see if the food tastes better if it has less salt in it.'

Sylvia finally gives me back the salt, but I can see exactly what is going to happen now.

'Ugh ... this is horrible!' She pulls a face as she takes her first mouthful. She continues. 'You over-salted it I'm afraid, my dear.'

Her behaviour is just like a child's. If there is an obvious mistake, something wrong, or in poor taste, it has nothing to do with her. Naturally, I am the one to blame.

I decide to carry out a little experiment. I gently remind her that she is the one who used too much salt to make the food less boring and suggest that perhaps it was because she could not see what was coming out of the salt cellar – I want to add something in her defence. It would be easy to accept the blame myself; it does not really matter who spoilt the once tasty food, but I just wonder if she can understand the connection – at least for a short while – between her actions and their consequences.

She slowly turns back to her plate, takes a look at it, then at the fork, then back to her plate. Suddenly she starts to mix the food together, combining the less salty part with the over-salted one. She loads up her fork, lifts it to her mouth, hesitates for just a moment and then proudly starts chewing her food with determined enjoyment.

In fact, she ate up everything on her plate. In spite of the criticism she often directs at the food I put on the table, she always manages to eat it all. In this instance, as soon as she understood that the fiasco she wanted to blame me for was actually the result of her own action, her mind amended the scenario immediately in a subconscious desire to resist accepting that she had done anything wrong. By eating the whole of her plate of food she deliberately demonstrated that she liked it that way, that it was what she wanted originally and that she had not made a mistake with the salt.

By the time I had finished washing the dishes that day, of course, there was no sign of any recall of lunch or our conversation. The day continued but I did feel a twinge of conscience deep inside as I had not stopped Sylvia eating her over-salted food. I made sure I gave her plenty to drink for the rest of the day.

CHAPTER
3

IT IS NOT GOING TO
WORK THIS WAY!

There were three nightdresses flapping on the washing line. They were gently dancing in the pleasant early September breeze, bathed in sparkling afternoon sunshine. In the seven months that had passed since my arrival as Sylvia's live-in carer I had learnt so much about Sylvia and about myself. I stopped for a moment and pondered the dancing clothes that I had hung out in the garden just a short while ago, on the clothesline tied between two old trees. I looked at them and I knew all their secrets.

In the previous few days, as a result of three different incidents, these three nightdresses had ended up in the laundry basket after being carefully and separately packed up, following the strict rules for the 'storage and cleaning of linen contaminated with bodily fluid'.

It felt rather grotesque that when staring at them I could not enjoy the dew-fresh, fragrant and clean reality of that moment. I could not help it; my mind was full of memories. What I saw was not the articles of clothing, two blue and one pink, but brown and yellow symbols of different body fluids that had appeared on all three garments as a consequence of each accident.

My most intense memory was from the most recent scenario. The pink, flowery, long-sleeved nightdress had fallen victim to a massive amount of smelly urine earlier that day, at around three o'clock in the morning.

I do not really remember how long it has taken me to realise that what I can hear is a squeaky, wailing, staccato voice, crying.

I know I have to wake up. It takes only seconds for my mind to register the message: 'Sylvia is in trouble.'

My conscience urges me, 'Go and check on her,' but longing to stay in bed, my inner voice counters, 'No, I'll wait another minute, maybe she'll sort herself out.' For a short moment I allow my head, already starting to feel tense, to fall back on to the tempting pillow.

It is not unusual for her to wander at night. She shuffles around the house, takes a rest in the living room, checks all the rooms of her property until finally drowsiness and fatigue win and she finds her way back to her bedroom without needing any help.

I start to count and promise myself: 'If I get to ten and she is still making a noise, I'll go and see her.' The wailing stops and I can hear that she is on the move so there cannot be a huge drama. I allow myself to think that the situation has settled itself when the silence of my bedroom is suddenly shattered by three fairly strong knocks on my wall.

I spring up, open my bedroom door and then Sylvia's door right next to it. She is sitting on the floor just inside the doorway to her bedroom, with her nightdress rucked up underneath her and her soaking wet pull-up pants halfway down her legs. She looks up at me impatiently, waiting for help.

'What has happened?' I am not at my best at this extremely early hour and I cannot mask my annoyance.

'I've had a fall,' she says, holding up her arms, her eyes silently beseeching me for help.

I switch the light on in her dark bedroom and in a second, like a good detective, I assess the situation.

Everything movable from the bedside table is now lying randomly all over the floor: her glass, books, lamp and reading glasses. She obviously wanted to go to the toilet, but lost her balance in the dark and grabbed everything that was close to her to try and prevent her fall. I quickly start to clear the obstacles from the floor so that I can help her up. Sylvia is shouting out and demanding my help, crying hysterically.

Just a few minutes ago I was fast asleep, dreaming deeply. Now my mind is fully awake and bursting with hundreds of rules of procedure for a situation like this, tense with the pressure of my position of responsibility.

I ask her to stay exactly where she is but she starts to slide on her bottom along the floor, using her arms for support, out of her room, into the corridor and towards the living room. I quickly call out, I admit in a rather sharp and scolding way: 'You have only yourself to thank for everything that has just happened if you don't use your walking-stick and don't keep the night-light on. No wonder you had a fall.'

My criticism just inspires her to continue sliding with the same odd technique, faster and more desperately this time, leaving a deep yellow urine mark behind on the light-coloured carpet in the corridor.

It is not going to work this way, I quickly realise. I take a deep breath, change the tone of my voice and start to give her simple but firm instructions. I need to be able to check that she has not injured herself and get her safely back to bed.

'Can you bend your knees?'

'Have you got any pain?'

'Lift your arm up to here, please.'

It works instantly. She listens to my commands, cooperates and dutifully does what I ask. My actions are supported by an angelic face on the outside, but what I really feel inside is quite the opposite.

The responsibility ticks inside me like a time bomb and makes my stomach churn. I must not stop my stream of instructions for a second.

Carers of people with dementia have an enormous responsibility. They are responsible for the actions of someone who has no idea what or why they are doing something and that something is then forgotten in a very short while.

In the advanced stages of dementia, basic logic has disappeared a long while ago. Searching for reasonable explanations is nothing more than barking up the wrong tree. Of course there are correlations between behaviour, actions and reactions, but it is very rare that the same situation or incident happens again under the same circumstances.

In the earlier stages of the disease, it is helpful to use a 'multiple stage' technique to try to unravel the reasons for a sudden change in behaviour logically.

Often it is an unmet physical need: needing to go to the toilet, an uncomfortable item of clothing, low blood sugar levels, or most obviously, though it is a reason that is frequently ignored, simply boredom.

Other common causes can be tiredness, both physical and mental – they go hand in hand most of the time anyway – occurring mainly in the afternoon as a consequence of being active up until that time, or the change in behaviour can be due to 'sundown syndrome', when the only reason for agitation or sadness seems to be the fact that the light is fading. The sun going down could perhaps be associated with any number of horrible things that took place in the dark.

If carers put themselves in the situation of those with the condition, it makes their behaviour easier to understand. It is considered normal to need peace and quiet, comfort and pleasure, after a day at work. If the day has been difficult and draining, and is followed by further negative experiences, naturally stress and agitation levels rise, patience levels drop and the ability to focus on anything is decreased.

Exactly the same applies to people living with dementia. The only difference is that their agitation and reaction to negative stimuli are much greater because, in the majority of cases, they are not able to express or even comprehend their needs and therefore these needs are unmet. What people with the disease do not understand they cannot explain.

Knowledge about this mental condition is therefore fundamental if we are caring for someone affected by it. My preferred course of action is to try and pre-empt and so prevent any of the avoidable causes of a sudden change in behaviour. How do I do it? By reminding and asking questions, and reminding and asking questions over and over again: 'Can I suggest going to the toilet?' 'Are you in the mood for a chocolate biscuit?' 'Would you like to have a short lie-down, just for half an hour?'

The number of possible questions is infinite as, in person-centred care, it is natural that the way to deal with an individual with dementia is different and unique for every single person. It is also essential to remember that these acute problems can differ a great deal, and what causes discomfort, leading to tension and agitation, and finally resulting in an acute problem, can change from day to day.

I keep speaking calmly and continue to give clear instructions. Luckily Sylvia has not sustained any injuries at all and is very fortunate to have strong bones. The majority of people of her age suffer from osteoporosis and even a minor accident or fall usually results in several broken bones. Finally she is able to stand up by herself.

While I clean and comfort her, and replace her nightdress and pads with fresh new ones, I look back at what has happened and try to think how I could have prevented her fall. Should I creep in and check that the night-light is on every night after she has gone to sleep, and several times in the night?

I settle Sylvia back down in her bed. She is still snivelling a bit, so I stay for a while. When she is quiet, I use my sweetest, most gentle tone of voice to explain to her again exactly why it is so important to leave her night-light on for the rest of the night.

She agrees.

I say good night to her and, seemingly serenely, close the door behind me, but my heart starts thumping now that I am alone with my thoughts. The potential damage and the injuries that could have resulted from what had happened in the last two hours hit me as a sort of aftershock.

To manage my stress – like mentally stretching after a thorough workout – I pack up and store her contaminated clothes, set about cleaning up all the mess she has left behind on the corridor carpet, and then finally clean myself up.

I do not feel sleepy at all, but there is still enough time to go back to bed before morning. I lie down on my back, staring at the ceiling and keeping my ears open for noises coming from the neighbouring room.

'Click.'

Instantly I identify the source of this sound and what has caused it.

Sylvia has just switched her night-light off.

CHAPTER
4

WHO HAS BEEN FIRED FROM THE FACTORY?

How the brain works, a very logical and straightforward article produced by Alzheimer's Australia,[2] gives a clear and basic introduction to the brain dysfunction involved in dementia and always helps me to picture what is going on inside of the head of someone affected by this disease. The article explains that the brain can be thought of as a factory and that the factory runs at peak efficiency when all the parts are working.

At the front of this factory (the frontal lobes) are the directors. They make plans for the factory and decide on who is going to do what and when. As things get underway they get feedback or other information as to how well things are going and they make judgements on what looks good and what does not look so good. Then they make further decisions, to change that or to keep this, and show their appreciation and annoyance. Planning, organising, judging, decision-making and appreciation therefore take place at the front of the brain.

In the middle of the factory (the parietal association cortex) are the managers. Each manager runs his/her own department. The left side is the talking side: there is a speech department that moves the throat, tongue and lip muscles, a language department that is responsible for finding the words you want and knowing the words' meaning, a music department, and various other departments. The right side is the picture side, with a motor department that helps you find your way around a building, knows where you are when you are driving a car, puts your arm through the sleeve of your coat, and so on.

The directors pass their plans on to the managers, and the managers make sure the directors' plans are carried out. In order to do this, directors and managers communicate freely with one another, sending messages back and forth.

At the bottom of the factory (the limbic region, amygdala and basal ganglia) are the workers. They do not know what the directors' plans are, but they know their job and they do that same job day in, day out. They take care of things like appetite control, the need for water, staying alert and awake or going to sleep, as well as basic emotions, such as turning on tears, making the face red and increasing the pulse rate.

When brain damage occurs, basically someone gets sacked. It can be the director, a manager or a worker, depending on where the damage takes place. Someone can also go on temporary leave of absence – for example, when there is a temporary swelling or loss of blood supply in the brain that is reversed in a short time.

The result of any injury, whether permanent or temporary, is that the efficiency of the factory is reduced. Messages are sent but are not picked up. Directors get annoyed. The managers get tired and the emotional workers get overwrought. Confusion reigns.

Understanding who has been fired and who is still on the job can help in interpreting the behaviour of people living with dementia.

■ ■ ■

Two days after Sylvia fell out of bed, Linda popped in to talk to her mother and remind her why it is so important to leave the night-light on when it is dark at night. She read my report of the incident and is always a great support when it comes to trying to convince Sylvia of anything.

The service provided by the professional carer is all about prevention and that is the aim of the written incident report too. It gives managers and also family members a guide, so that they can analyse and evaluate what has happened, make new arrangements if necessary and put practical actions in place to prevent similar incidents occurring in the future.

When Linda is here, Sylvia is always bright and smiling. She shows an interest in nearly everything and her sense of comfort is noticeably stronger at these times.

Sylvia nods rapidly to express her agreement when Linda asks her to leave the night-light on and acts as if this is the first time that anyone has ever said anything on the subject to her. Her reaction shows that she understands the importance of the night-light in preventing her having another fall.

When Linda finally leaves, her mother and I continue with our usual daily routine. We have dinner together and then sit down in the living room to watch Sylvia's favourite shows until she gets tired and is ready for bed.

The TV shows that really win Sylvia's attention are Murder, She Wrote, Poirot *and* Miss Marple, *but, however good the programmes are, I must admit that I have become bored by seeing the same episodes over and over again. It is not the storyline that actually entertains Sylvia, as she cannot really follow it. It is rather that the main characters and the familiar faces and voices make her feel comfortable while she is watching them, as they have made their place in her damaged mind forever. We have the boxed sets, but the way some TV channels keep playing Sylvia's best-loved episodes over and over again almost gives the impression that they specialise in catering for an audience living with dementia.*

We watch, with massive enthusiasm on Sylvia's part and enforced enthusiasm on mine, and I keep answering the same questions: 'So tell me, what is happening now?' 'What did she say?' 'Does it make any sense to you, love?' It could be worse though. Many other live-in carers have to watch the financial news and read economics magazines out loud all day long, as that is what the person who they are looking after is interested in.

Finally Sylvia stands up and says she feels tired so is going to hit the hay. A few minutes later I follow her into her bedroom to help her with the few things she cannot do herself. When she is eventually in bed I check that the night-light is on. She wants me to turn it off.

In my most velvety voice I explain yet again what the aim of the night-light is and what the main thing is that we want to prevent by leaving it on, namely her having a fall. She listens to me patiently and when I finish, she again asks me to switch it off.

'I cannot do that, Sylvia,' I reply. 'Linda asked me to make sure it is on all night.'

'When did you meet her?' she asks, totally surprised.

'A few hours ago,' I say. 'She spoke to both of us.'

'I want to talk to her right now. I need to ask her why this stupid light needs to be on. I cannot sleep like this.'

I can feel the pressure building up inside me and wonder if that is what it feels like when you are about to have a stroke, but I know if I am tense I will just make things worse and produce unnecessary problems for Sylvia and for myself. I am feeling really angry inside though. I am starting to wonder if anyone can survive caring for a person with dementia full time with an intact mind. It's not late, so I dial Linda's number.

'Hello.' Linda's husband Kevin picks up the phone.

Linda is not at home, but he agrees to back me up. It might just help to persuade Sylvia if she hears the same message about the importance of adequate lighting in the night from a third party who is also a close relative.

As soon as Sylvia hears Kevin's voice, she takes her kindest voice out of her magic hat and also nods vigorously. I cannot hear what Kevin is saying on the other end of the line, but no matter how Sylvia is reacting to his words, she does not fool me.

The conversation ends, I make sure the night-light is still on and say good night. There is nothing more to say. I leave her room and shut the door. I stay outside for a minute. Before sixty seconds are up I hear her switch the night-light off. Sylvia's room is in darkness again.

Wilfulness and stubbornness are not attractive qualities at the best of times, but if a wilful and stubborn person has impaired judgement and is physically unable to achieve even simple tasks, he or she can sometimes easily seem to be both a hopeless and an unattractive human being.

When I next broached the subject of the night-light, Sylvia said she did not care even if Her Majesty the Queen decreed she should leave the night-light on, she would not do it, and that she would never be able to sleep that way. At that moment my temper and frustration made me feel that I was no longer looking at a fragile and vulnerable old lady. The uncharitable thought even crossed my mind that it was a shame she did not remember crawling on the floor asking for my help after her last fall – a vivid picture that, whether I wanted to or not, I could not get out of my mind. I felt that she was deliberately opposing me and trying to aggravate me, but as I calmed down, I soon conceded that that was not true.

Those living with dementia are not able to understand the link between cause and effect anymore. They cannot think that if I do this then that will be the consequence, and arguing with them does no good. The fact that people with this disease do not manipulate has been clinically proven, as the part of the brain responsible for logical thinking is no longer (or only partly) functioning in this condition.

Although I am only too aware of this fact and accept it, in certain situations I have to force myself to keep it in mind. When I do make that conscious effort in difficult circumstances, each time I feel I am taking a huge step forward in my care of people with this condition and in my understanding of them, as it is so easy to forget. Patience and time are the carer's (and the person with dementia's) best friends on their journey together, and if one keeps making one's observations accurately, the 'whys' are suddenly answered, and sooner or later the thunderclouds of anger and the mists of misunderstanding clear.

■ ■ ■

Several days after Linda's visit in which she had emphasised the importance of the night-light, Sylvia said something in passing which made it clear she was extremely worried about saving energy in the house. I felt it explained everything.

It did not help reminding her of the solar panels on the roof and stressing that energy does not cost that much because of modern energy-efficient systems. Sylvia's still intact memories are years behind the present and she cannot cope with the concept of the relatively new energy source of solar power. Her mind sticks to its old habits and knowledge, completely erases any new information and keeps repeating, 'You must save energy.'

As Sylvia became more and more obsessed with switching everything off, I finally let the problem go. The night-light now stays off despite the risk of another fall in the middle of the night. I know that she was very lucky to get away with only one tiny bruise on the back of her thigh which showed a few days after her previous fall, but I have to accept that I cannot force her into doing something against her will, when she is determined to do what she wants.

I have learnt to handle Sylvia's reality in the same way that I expect other people to handle mine. Whenever I am tempted to change rather than gently bend her iron will, I simply imagine how it would feel if someone took my reality, re-formed it, transformed it, and then gave it back to me stating: 'This is your new reality from now on.' I must not interfere, as any harsh impact on her reality will only lead to new traumas.

I am therefore left consciously preparing spiritually, emotionally and physically for the worst. Thoughts about what I am supposed to do if she falls. Thoughts about calling an ambulance. That is how I go to sleep every night, in a sort of half-alert mode.

I am exhausted.

■ ■ ■

CHAPTER
5

SMALL VICTORIES

There are two feelings hula-hooping in my stomach while I watch Sylvia having lunch. I cannot decide which one is stronger, apathy or frustration, but whichever one it is, I am finding it difficult to have my own meal. She is eating vegetable and tomato soup with a spoon. As usual she is sitting a bit too far away from the table – she would not let me push her chair in closer – with a sparkling white napkin on her lap that does not suspect that it will be stained in seconds. Sylvia is on autopilot, gazing out of the window, looking out for birds.

I notice that she does not move her body towards the soup plate. Like an aristocrat, her body stays rigid and upright; it is only the spoon in her hand that moves back and forth between her mouth and the plate. Her movements would have been those of a high-born lady if she had not dripped the second spoon of deep orange liquid onto her lap. I think of offering to help her move closer to the table and suggesting that it might be better if she sits straight, not sideways as she has taken to sitting lately, almost as if she is sitting side-saddle.

My thoughts turn to Sue, who left about two hours ago. She starts cleaning the house at half past nine every Tuesday morning, mainly focusing on the kitchen and Sylvia's bedroom. She then takes Sylvia out for a morning coffee so that I can strip and change Sylvia's bed, and put fresh new towels in her bathroom. The smell and look of the house are always transformed into something very pleasant after Sue's visit. That is why lunch is hurting so much.

I try to avoid looking at Sylvia, but my eyes separate from my mind and satisfy their curiosity involuntarily. I cannot take them off her. Every second spoon of soup misses her mouth and lands on her light-green trousers, the floor or the white napkin. The crumbs from the slice of toast served on her side plate have already spread within a metre circle of her. Unconsciously my mind wonders if she doing it all deliberately, but my rational mind knows the answer.

I realise that I have changed a lot about my approach since I came to care for Sylvia a year ago. I now know that if I ask her directly, she will refuse to change her position. She feels patronised, and simply because I suggest something, she will not do it. Sentences beginning with phrases such as: 'Don't you think it would be better' or 'I don't know, but I just thought I'd ask you' usually have a better outcome, so I decide to use that approach now.

There is no physical problem that prevents Sylvia from eating nicely. It is obvious that her body remembers the movements; her basic intention is to transfer the food from her plate to her mouth.

The same happens when Sylvia goes to the café at George's Farm.

She usually orders a slice of cake with her latte, and every time without fail one third of it lands everywhere but in her mouth. I used to feel embarrassed when I first started taking her there because we always left a great mess behind, but then I noticed that everybody knows her, and now everybody knows me too. The staff know what to expect and see it as part of their job, a necessary extra. As they wave Sylvia goodbye they have already grabbed all the cleaning equipment they need and are on their way to our table.

The contrast between her extremely proud body posture – she holds her head erect and always decorously dabs her lipstick-covered mouth carefully with her napkin after each mouthful – and the mess she produces never fails to shock the onlooker. It is tempting to think that she does not care, but I know this is not true and that she would care if she were aware of the mess she makes when she eats. She really has no clue about what she is actually doing, so there is no use trying to correct her. I also know that if I were to tell her, it would only make things worse. In my view the problem is caused by damaged movement coordination and lack of judgement, neither of which she or I can do anything about.

My role as Sylvia's carer is to maintain her dignity as far as is possible, so I use my best endeavours to make sure that she is quickly restored to her usual clean and tidy self after she has eaten anything in public or at home.

Never argue with someone who has dementia as you can never win is a golden rule that is always underlined in dementia-care training. The mind of a person with the disease deletes what it cannot cope with, so the responsibility remains the carer's. If anything happens to the person with dementia, the carer is the one to take the blame and is the only one who can lose.

Looking back over the twelve months I have been Sylvia's live-in carer I can see that only now do I really understand the truth of this statement. There is no doubt that during the previous year Sylvia has enjoyed her victories, but I have relished my small victories too, and I am not proud of the fact. I find it disconcerting to admit how much my childish and sometimes even malicious little victories used to restore me.

I remember a particularly disturbed night followed by a very taxing and draining morning after which I had had to use every drop of resourcefulness to ensure that Sylvia reached her afternoon's dental check-up on time. She does not like going to the dentist.

The dentist asks me to stay with Sylvia because of her condition. Checking and cleaning her teeth takes only ten minutes and the treatment is not painful at all, but still Sylvia winces and jumps every few seconds as the little electric tool rakes her teeth.

I know that she is overreacting, and that nothing the dentist is doing can possibly be hurting her, but at the same time as I am reassuring her, I realise I am secretly gloating, a hidden smile on my face strictly invisible to others, feeling that I have got even with her after the considerable challenges of the previous twelve hours.

Most people identify walking as a relaxing and pleasant leisure activity, but going for a walk can be a pleasure and a punishment at the same time.

The thought of going for a walk in the area near Sylvia's house conjures up an idyllic picture of strolling by the river in the sunshine on a lovely day with a gentle breeze blowing. The sails of dozens of boats are flapping proudly on the busy waterway, enormous freighters are being loaded at the port and the sharp sound of the seagulls indicates that the sea is near.

Sylvia loves all these things. She was brought up by the sea and used to enjoy sitting on a bench for hours watching the water and the birds. The sound of the waves washing the coastline always brings a smile to her face.

One afternoon, when the weather looked nice from inside the house, I asked Sylvia if she would like to go for a walk by the river and to my surprise she happily agreed. I helped her into the car and we headed for Felixstowe, a charming seaside town about 25 miles away.

I am not prepared for the strong, freezing-cold breeze that faces us when we finally get out of the car at the coast. Surprisingly, Sylvia does not protest as she is a real 'coldie'. Perhaps she is focusing on keeping her balance. Luckily she is wearing her winter coat – she only leaves it off when the weather gets really hot in the summer – so she will not be harmed by it.

After walking away from the car for only a few minutes, Sylvia asks if we can go home.

'All right, we need to turn back then, as the car is over there,' I reply.

She instantly starts an argument, adamant that we are walking in the right direction and that we will be able to get to the car if we continue on the same path. She becomes verbally aggressive, raising her voice and using a loud, lecturing tone. I decide not to correct her as I do not want the argument to escalate. Sylvia is mobile and warmly dressed, and I enjoy walking, so I let her lead me forwards knowing we are walking further and further away from our desired destination. I feel a secret sense of satisfaction. Touché!

In the end of course I feel sorry for her and, using a different approach, I finally manage to persuade her where the car is. We change direction and when we eventually get back, I hear her sighing 'Thank goodness' as she is at last able to sit down in the passenger seat, protected from the wind.

The seemingly innocent opening phrase 'Do you remember when …?' is very common in everyday conversation, but it is positively cruel to start a sentence in this way when you are talking to someone living with dementia. Of course they do not remember – that is the very essence of their condition. I actively avoid using this phrase now, but when I started to care for Sylvia I used to use it quite often and I know I used to have a touch of sarcasm in my voice that only I (I hope) would be able to detect when I put the question to her.

Did I really want to punish her? I don't rightly know. It may have been because I had to repeat everything a lot, especially when Sylvia unexpectedly turned into a monster and was verbally aggressive or challenging, but it was definitely a sort of revenge and it brought me an inexplicable satisfaction to be attacking her with an invisible weapon. I am relieved to think that no one would ever have noticed my unworthy attempt to get back at Sylvia as such a common turn of phrase just seemed to be a polite conversational gambit. Like anyone else listening, Sylvia was never aware of the malice behind my words: my revenge was illusory.

Small victories gained at Sylvia's expense may be empty victories, but a carer is under a huge amount of pressure and techniques that relieve this pressure are invaluable. Heaven can turn into hell in a minute on some days, when it suddenly becomes extremely hard to deal with someone with the disease. When this person is especially argumentative, when nothing is good enough and negative comments are made about everything, it is essential to remember that as a carer, you are a human being as well. If you have been dealing with dementia for countless days in a row, getting up every single day to care for a stubborn and very strong character for up to 24 hours a day, patience becomes a real treasure because you have less and less of it as time goes on.

'Snake charming' is the term I use to describe the techniques I rely on in difficult circumstances. No two scenarios are ever the same, but I have a great reservoir of methods and ideas that I draw on and continually add to, as my creativity is challenged by the condition of dementia over and over again.

However, sometimes nothing will persuade Sylvia to do what she does not want to do. When she was not in the mood for her morning shower recently, I tried everything and brought out all my tricks hoping that finally I would be able to get her under the water. I had no success. No matter what I said, suggested or did, she always had some new objection that she used to avoid or delay it. Her shower that day had to be at a time of her choosing, not mine, and she eventually had it just before lunch.

■ ■ ■

Sometimes it is as if Sylvia has somehow got herself stuck somewhere and cannot escape. My job is similar to a breakdown lorry arriving to help a car stranded in the middle of nowhere. I have all the tools and equipment that I need, but I still have to keep trying out different ideas until I diagnose the real problem and find the solution. Once the fault or faults have been fixed, the car can function again as usual, at least for a while.

Sylvia has an electric blanket to keep her bed nice and warm. No wonder, then, that one particularly cold morning my attempts at getting her out of bed and into her shower were rudely rejected and I was repeatedly told, 'Leave me alone!' or 'Go away!'

I finally achieve a breakthrough when I remind her that she might want to go to the toilet and she accepts the invitation to try to spend a penny. (The toilet is in the same room as the shower.) After she has gone into her en suite and shut the door, I immediately put on my rubber gloves and get a plastic bag ready for her clothes.

A long time ago she accepted the fact that I sometimes knock on the bathroom door when she is on the toilet in order to assist her with her personal hygiene if necessary. So this is what I do. She gives me permission to come in and is still sitting down on the lavatory. Although the shower is staring at her from only a metre away, I do not mention anything about a shower, not even the word 'water', but my plan is to ensure that she does not leave the bathroom without taking a shower.

It's now or never! Having managed to get this far, I am determined not to give up.

I pretend that every word I say is just a small matter only and by using the 'magic words' I conduct her movements, while closely watching and observing her reactions to my instructions, in order to know how far I can go.

'Shall I take this off?' I point to her nightdress, explaining that it makes it easier to move around without it.

'Do you mind if I take these too? I would like to give you clean ones.' With a quick movement, her disposable pull-up pants are off.

'Is it OK to take your slippers off? You don't want them getting wet in the shower, do you?'

As I mention the word 'shower' for the first time, I set the hot water running so that the little bathroom is filled with warmth and steam. I see that Sylvia wants to step under it and finally she does, moving into the middle of the shower area and enjoying every second of being under the hot water.

By the time Sylvia has finished, my energy levels have already dropped drastically and this is just the beginning of the day. I may no longer see things in terms of winning or losing, but the score 'Sylvia: 1, Me: Nil' does flash up in my mind.

As a carer gets to know the person living with dementia it becomes clear that there is no need at all for victories, small or large. I have learnt a lot in the time I have been caring for Sylvia and my resilience is noticeably stronger and more developed. It takes time to learn about another person, no matter whether they are healthy or ill; there is a personality to deal with and to get to know. It is naturally a time-consuming process.

As well as getting to know the person you are caring for, it is vital to observe the changes in his or her condition. Sylvia's condition has deteriorated in the past twelve months. Confusion manifests itself in a thousand ways and it is there constantly, every single day. Sometimes her thoughts and actions are not synchronised as the gaps between the brain cells that give the commands and the brain cells that carry the messages are just simply too big.

The problem can be illustrated by a simple analogy. When people stand in a circle, relatively close to each other, and pass a ball around the circle without changing their position, it is a really simple task, but as soon as you take a few people out of the circle, the task becomes more difficult. If you then increase the number of people taken out of the circle, the people left have to make a considerable effort to make sure that the ball reaches the next person without being dropped.

The ball represents the message from the brain cells. The people in the circle represent the brain cells that carry the message to the appropriate body parts. In Sylvia's case, there are very few people left in the circle. The distances are unconquerable and the message has no chance of reaching its destination.

Not only is Sylvia's confusion increasing in general, it also increases greatly as the day goes by. Tiredness has a serious effect on her mental state, so that everything usually becomes much worse by late afternoon or early evening. A rise in confusion sometimes results in broken sentences and apparently irrational behaviour, where speech and action do not conform; for example, she says, 'I am going to bed now' when she is actually coming out of her bedroom.

In situations like this, I try to guess the original intention and decide whether to take what she says or the action and her body language into account. With experience I've learnt to recognise that what makes this task more difficult is my own current mood. If I am calm and relaxed, I have the energy, good humour and patience to take time to investigate the mismatch between her words and actions using simple questions, trying to clarify what she really wants. If I am tired and feeling less patient, I take her at her word and employ the well-worked routine, gestures and signs to simply manoeuvre her into bed.

This may seem like a practical solution, but every time I choose this course of action, I pay the price if that is not what Sylvia wanted to do. If she is not 100 per cent relaxed at bedtime, it will have an effect on her nocturnal activity. She cannot resolve most of her problems on her own – in fact practically none of them – so sooner or later she needs me to help. The whole 'get her into bed quickly' routine therefore backfires and all I am doing is creating extra tasks for myself, not to mention the certainty of a disturbed night.

Having done the maths I realise that it is worthwhile paying attention to anything that might be bothering Sylvia and that I must take time to meet all her needs before she settles down for the night, even if it means I have to pretend and put on an act to persuade her that everything is fine in order to calm her down. It is interesting that Sylvia, who is usually sensitive to every tiny mood change of mine, does not notice if my kindness, politeness or exaggerated tone of voice is just pretence. Also, as well as keeping Sylvia's emotional highs and lows under control by successfully concealing my tension or bad mood, strangely enough just acting out my improved mood has an instantly positive effect on me and changes my attitude at once.

■ ■ ■

We always have something new to learn, but in the course of my training and work in the world of dementia I have learnt a tremendous amount not just about the condition itself, but about myself too. I know now how to keep not only Sylvia's but also my own restless spirit in balance and how to react most effectively to the challenges, targeting the actual problem and getting Sylvia out of the latest situation she has got herself into.

With experience, facing the challenges of caring for a person with dementia when they arise does not take as much of an effort as it did in the past, because every day you add to the huge range of solutions that are stored in your mind. However, all these tools and tricks, together with the understanding that becomes an integral part of a professional carer, are worth nothing without love, passion and respect.

CHAPTER
6

TERRIFYING NUMBERS

There are over 850,000 people with dementia in the UK and, according to the Alzheimer's Society,[3] the figure will rise to over a million people living with the condition by 2025; it is estimated that one in six people aged over 80 have the disease and that at present, only 44 per cent of people with dementia in England, Wales and Northern Ireland receive a diagnosis. The current annual financial cost is over £26 billion and the value to the country of the work done by family carers is over £11 billion. Two-thirds of people with this condition live in the community while one third live in a care home. Altogether, 80 per cent of all the people living in care homes have a form of dementia or severe memory problems.[3]

In my experience, there is a great need to increase public awareness about the disease. Despite the fact that anybody I talk to about my work knows someone – a family member, friend or neighbour – who shows typical symptoms of the condition and has amusing stories about 'funny forgetfulness', changes in behaviour, and not so amusing stories about decreased personal hygiene and hallucinations, the majority of the people concerned have not yet had dementia diagnosed.

Alzheimer's disease is the most commonly recognised cause of dementia. However, dementia is not one condition but a term which encompasses a range of conditions characterised by impairment of brain functions, including language, memory, perception, personality and cognitive skills. It can lead to a loss of understanding, rationality, social skills and normal emotional reaction.

More than 100 different types of dementia are now recognised, but Alzheimer's disease still remains the most common, accounting for around 60 per cent of all dementia in England. Alzheimer's disease is caused by changes in the structure of the brain and a shortage of essential chemicals that help with the transmission of messages. The ongoing death of brain cells leads to insuperable gaps in the brain structure between the neurons (nerve cells) and different brain regions.

Parkinson's disease is another well-known condition often associated with dementia. People living with Parkinson's disease don't have enough of a chemical called dopamine because some nerve cells in their brain have died. Without dopamine people can find that their movements become slower and less controlled so it takes longer to do things and dementia is more common in people with Parkinson's than those without.[4]

Other common forms of dementia are vascular dementia, where the brain structure has been damaged because of problems with the supply of blood to the brain, such as a series of small strokes, and dementia with Lewy bodies (DLB), where tiny deposits of protein in the nerve cells in the brain result in a loss of connection between them. Mixed dementia is where a person has more than one form of dementia at the same time: Alzheimer's disease with vascular dementia is the most common form, but a person with mixed dementia can also have DLB as well as these two forms of dementia.

It holds true for most of the conditions associated with dementia that they are typically progressive, degenerative and irreversible, and there is currently no cure. The occurrence, type and severity of the symptoms largely depend on the type of dementia, the stage of the disease, and the damage caused to the brain structure. For example, a person with mild dementia may only experience one or two symptoms that have a relatively minor impact on day-to-day living, while a person in the late stages of dementia may require 24-hour care because of the severity of his or her symptoms. The early signs of dementia are usually subtle and not always obviously abnormal either to the individual or to family and friends. By the time someone receives a diagnosis, it is only by examining the damage to the brain structure (using scanning techniques) that can give an approximate idea of when the disease actually started.

Early signs can be more frequent forgetfulness or unusual difficulties in everyday tasks, such as making a cup of coffee or tea that never used to cause the slightest problems before. Other signs include changes in communication skills; struggling to remember common words and expressions; loss of language; disorientation in time and space; impaired judgement and physical coordination; more frequent occurrence of household accidents, such as spilled coffee and broken glasses; learning and concentration difficulties; altered sleeping patterns; eating disturbances, such as difficulty in swallowing or a change in appetite; and screaming. Depression, self-isolation and apathy also go hand in hand with dementia.

■ ■ ■

Sylvia's daughter first noticed that something was wrong when her mother got lost on a route that she had walked 100 times before. Sylvia and her daughter live in a small village only one street apart.

When Linda rang her mother up and they agreed to meet at their usual spot at the corner in five minutes' time one day, she was distraught when she arrived and her mother was not there. She rushed to Sylvia's house, but could not find her. She then started walking along the main road in the opposite direction away from her own house, asking locals if they had seen her mother. She did not have to walk far. Sylvia was sitting on the bench in the bus shelter and was most surprised to see that her daughter was so upset when she came closer and greeted her. Sylvia did not understand Linda's anxiety and her questioning as to why she had not waited at the spot where they had agreed to meet.

This kind of incident and other seemingly minor changes in behaviour are warning signs to family and friends and it is crucial that they take the time to listen and observe, and that they also listen to their inner voice, the whisper of their senses, saying 'something is not right here.'

Except for changes in brain structure as a result of physical trauma, such as a stroke or embolism when the normal blood flow to the brain is obstructed, the cause of most types of dementia is unknown, but what research has shown is that some people are more disposed to get dementia than others.

Various risk factors can increase the likelihood of a person developing dementia, such as simply getting older, a person's genes, if they suffer from diabetes, if they make certain lifestyle choices. For example, Korsakoff's syndrome is a relatively rare form of dementia that is caused by excessive and prolonged alcohol consumption.

Some people mistakenly think that dementia is a normal part of ageing. It is not. Not everyone getting old will lose their mental capacity or memories. However, even if we live a totally healthy life, use our brain constantly, continue learning and do all sorts of physical exercise, there is no guarantee that we will avoid dementia.

Before the disease struck, Sylvia was highly intelligent and spoke four languages fluently. In fact, she still uses German or French expressions, mostly during meals or when she says thank you for something. During WW2 she worked at Bletchley Park as a code-breaker and later she became a highly successful designer in the fashion industry. She travelled a lot, was well educated and broad-minded.

She has retained some memories, mainly from deep in the past, but I need all my skills and knowledge of her past life to identify the real memories and the memories which are a mutation of reality born out of real past events and recent ones that have become combined in her mind to create something unique.

Some of Sylvia's memories lie so deep that no disease could ever erase them from her brain, and I will never be able to erase them from my brain either. There is a German tongue-twister that I will remember for the rest of my life as she shares it with me at least five times a day, proudly finishing each recitation flawlessly – she never stumbles or makes a mistake. Even if I were woken up from my deepest sleep I would be able to recite it too, although I have absolutely no knowledge of German. It is indelibly etched in my memory.

'Have I told you this saying?' Sylvia asks me as I help her get ready for the day. Before I have a chance to answer, she fluently recites her party piece.

'Herr von Hagen aus Remagen, darf ich's wagen Sie zu fragen, wieviel Kragen mit Behagen, ohne Zagen Sie getragen an den Tagen, als sie lagen, ihre Blagen, krank am Magen ohne Klagen auf dem Schragen im Spital zu Kopenhagen?'

She beams at me. 'Or there is another one. Do you want to hear it, dear?' she asks with a childlike, mischievous spark

*in her eyes as soon as she finishes reciting the tongue-twister.
I cannot say no.*

*'Herr von Hagen aus Remagen, darf ich's wagen Sie zu
fragen, wieviel Kragen mit Behagen, ohne Zagen Sie getragen
an den Tagen, als sie lagen, ihre Blagen, krank am Magen ohne
Klagen auf dem Schragen im Spital zu Kopenhagen?'*

■ ■ ■

CHAPTER
7

SURVIVAL TECHNIQUES

Sometimes I ask myself the question, why am I doing this? Working as a live-in carer is not a typical lifelong profession and is not one that you can keep doing for an extended period of time without burnout or depression. Whenever I talk about my job, people always ask me exactly the same question: 'How can anyone do your job for a long time without having a nervous breakdown?'

The truthful answer is that I feel I have a gift for speaking the language that uncovers an understanding of even the most challenging situations related to dementia. After only a couple of years of doing 24/7 dementia care, I realised that one of the best parts of my job was that every day brings a new challenge, a new mystery that I have to solve or decode.

Although I may spend years with the same person with dementia, perhaps doing the same routine or going to the same places, the current experience is always unique. So far I have spent almost two years with Sylvia, but the approach, the order of instructions or movements, the mood, the weather, they all differ all the time; one day we are singing together in the car, other days I have to wade through a grumpy mood to find 'my Sylvia' who will finally agree to come out with me so that we can do the shopping together. That said, in order to be able to continue doing this type of care work for this amount of time, I have had to develop my very own survival tools and techniques, without which I would have broken down long ago. I have seen a lot of carers turn their backs on very confused people with dementia after looking after them for only a day or two. Their explanations for leaving are simple: 'I don't need this.' 'I can't do it.' 'You must be kidding.' Yet by becoming part of the lives of people with this disease, and by understanding them and appreciating them, carers can bring about miracles, which will recharge their batteries so that they can survive on that energy during the days when things do not go so well.

It helps everyone caring for a person with dementia to be clear on some basic rules, and one of the most important survival techniques is knowledge itself. This knowledge is essential for all carers, whether they are professional carers or family members who have not chosen the profession: there are countless relatives who have taken over looking after a family member who has begun to show typical signs and symptoms of the condition and who are continuing with the caring role for as long as they are able.

Carers cannot look after a person with dementia well unless they have a detailed knowledge of the disease, the most common types of dementia, the effects on the brain, the range of symptoms and the possible behavioural changes. A thirst for basic knowledge opens the door into the fantastic but extremely complex world of dementia where there are hundreds more doors that will open the mind to thousands of specific topics related to the condition. The study of the condition is a lifelong learning experience. No matter how much experience of the disease carers have, they constantly meet new situations and problems.

The person-centred approach is very much the starting point in dementia care, and family members therefore have a definite advantage over professional carers.

When I first meet a person with dementia who is going to be in my care, I never look at the condition, I always look at the person behind it. First impressions are important and careful observation can make all the difference as to how things develop as far as the special relationship between the carer and the person being cared for is concerned. I try to create a quick sketch based on what the person wears, his or her personal hygiene, the gestures he or she uses, his or her ability to communicate, especially non-verbal communication. Then as time goes by I add more and more information in order to build up as full a picture as possible as a result of my personal experience in caring for them. It is imperative to know everything about the physical condition of the people in my care. What are they capable of doing and for how long? What is it that they like or used to like doing, and what did they do in the past before the disease took hold? Are they able to do it now? Can they see and hear properly?

As knowledge about both the condition and the person with dementia expands, so carers become increasingly confident about dealing with unexpected or challenging situations as well as recurring problems, habits and idiosyncrasies. Knowledge can include understanding the usefulness of alternative therapies, such as music therapy, art therapy or aromatherapy. It is also invaluable to find out about local leisure options, such as dance sessions for people living with the disease and their carers, or more gentle activities that elderly people with dementia can enjoy.

Naturally, there are days when batteries are dangerously low. Carers are human beings too after all, with their own personal problems.

All it takes is a bad night's sleep because of a headache and the next morning I have to start another nerve-racking day from a lower level of energy and patience than normal.

It is vitally important for carers to take control of their own problems and identify the best way to find the opportunities for a little 'me time' when they can be alone and recharge their batteries – 'me time' that will fit into the routine of the person with dementia.

I take advantage of some time away from Sylvia quite a few times each day. Before I go in search of some peace, I recognise her needs by telling her exactly what I am going to do and how long I am going to be away. It works for me if I use the 'I need to talk to my husband' excuse, saying that I am going to go to my room to phone him. The institution of marriage means a lot to Sylvia and if I remind her that my husband and I have to be apart a lot of the time because of my job, she often encourages me to go and do what I have to do to keep my marriage going and asks me to give him her love. If she comes to find me a few minutes later because she has forgotten what she was told, a quick reminder is usually enough and she politely leaves me alone for a bit longer.

When I need only a few seconds' break in order to take a deep breath, let out a sigh or a yell in order to break the tension that is making my stomach stiffen, I simply say I need to go to the loo. It is another thing that she understands; if nature calls you must go. Using this excuse, I can leave her alone for a short time without feeling guilty. Before she gets restless and comes looking for me, I will be back and keeping her company.

'Going with the flow' is another very useful practice. If you imagine yourself swimming upstream in a river, you get tired, you are constantly being pushed in the opposite direction from the way you want to go and in extreme circumstances you could even drown. Unless you are an Olympic swimmer, the flow eventually takes you where it wants and you cannot do anything about it. It sounds paradoxical, but although a carer is there to help and guide, actually the people with dementia are the ones in charge. They lead the carer wherever they want to go at any given moment. The carer's job is only to decide whether or not this way is safe for them.

Playing cards was Sylvia's idea and it is an excellent pastime for both of us. I have absolutely no problem with her in these half hours, or hours, depending on how long she remains interested in dealing, shuffling and cutting the cards. When it comes to rules, however, she takes a very liberal attitude, as was the case in our last game.

Sylvia deals out the cards and sternly explains that the total value of the cards has to be at least 50 before you can put them down on the table. However, as the game goes on, she changes the rules according to her hand of cards and their value. When she wants to get rid of her cards quickly, she tells me it is too boring to wait until we get to 50 after all, so from now on, we can put down any three cards if they match in colour or if they are a run. I do not correct or argue with her. Why should I? She is engrossed in the game and enjoys these moments.

Now she is fretting because she needs the seven of diamonds. Suddenly she starts speaking in German. For the rest of the game, as her excitement mounts, German is the language she uses. I assume that in the past she played card games with German friends and that speaking German evokes in her an agreeable sort of happiness linked to that time. She forgets to complain about anything, I just follow wherever her mind leads us and because the game pleases her, it pleases me too. When she is relaxed, my brain has a little free time too. I never point out that she is speaking another language. I respect whatever is most convenient for her when we play. I can follow the game anyway.

What I call our mealtime ritual is something I have learnt on the way and adjusted to suit Sylvia. I have to cut her food up for her as she has rheumatoid arthritis in her right hand so cannot do it herself. When I set the table for our very first meal, I automatically put a knife and fork on the table for each of us. As soon as she sat down at the table, she gave me her knife, explaining that she did not need it and that by not having it on the table we would be able to save on the washing-up. Nine out of ten people would have put only a fork in front of her at the next mealtime. I was one of the nine. The expression on her face immediately told me that I had made a huge mistake and I had seriously hurt her feelings. I tried to justify my actions.

'I am sorry. I just thought you wouldn't need the knife because I've already cut the meat up for you.'

'Yes, dear, but I am still here and I like to be treated as human being,' she replied.

I felt thoroughly ashamed. She was quite right. Since then, I always set her place with a fork and a knife.

As you can guess, our mealtime ritual is that she gives her knife back to me before she starts every meal with the comment that she will not be needing it. Putting out both a knife and a fork shows my respect for her and maintains her dignity by giving her choice, even though she chooses exactly the same option every time.

The ability to repress feelings is another survival tool. Carers have to repress their desires, interests, and longing for loved ones, family and friends as far as they possibly can. The relationship between a carer and a person with dementia is similar to that of a mother after giving birth to her first child: she puts her child first and represses everything else she wants or she needs, focusing only on the vulnerable baby, who depends completely on her.

I know I am quite impatient, certainly that is how my family would describe me. My mother is amazed that I am still doing this draining care work. I do not really know how it happens, but as soon as I am with a person who has this mental condition, some switch goes on in my brain. I imagine it is just like being an actor; actors describe a similar 'click' before they step onto the stage.

In contrast with how I have always behaved in my private life, now, when working as a professional carer, I suddenly become patient; I do not insist on anything I want if the person I am caring for wants something else; I never initiate an argument, or if the person with dementia initiates one I never react. I am very good at brushing things off, I do not take things personally and I know how to manoeuvre a way carefully through challenges or situations that at first seem hopeless.

However, it was only after experiencing a number of conflicts in my professional life that I reached this stage and there is a price to pay. In my case it is that I look for conflicts when I am on leave. Everything I have repressed comes up to the surface and I have to let it out, though, of course, I try to keep this within a tolerable range. I recognise that when I take a break I need to be spoiled and loved in order to be able to recharge my batteries and feel refreshed and full of energy for my return to the world of Mr Alzheimer where I am needed 24 hours a day, and where my skills are tested constantly by the dear souls I care for.

When I work, I have only two hours' official break within a day.

It is not much, especially if you cannot spend 120 minutes undisturbed. Sometimes visitors come to see Sylvia, which is great as my responsibility is taken from me and I can really relax. If I leave Sylvia to go shopping, although I am away from her physically, my mind keeps wondering what she might be doing, where is she putting things away that I will not find again for weeks and whether she is safe. It is not easy to switch off from being a carer.

I admit that I have used fibbing as a survival technique too when necessary, for Sylvia's and my own well-being. I do not encourage anybody to do this, but there are times when situations occur unexpectedly and carers have to make the decision. In order to avoid a problem and look after themselves and their own inner peace so that they can continue to be able to provide the care needed for the person with dementia, fibbing might be the answer. Just as in an emergency on an aeroplane, those travelling with children are instructed to put the oxygen mask on themselves first, before fitting them on the children. It makes perfect sense. If the parents cannot get oxygen, they will not be able to help the vulnerable children, who cannot make decisions for themselves. If I am running on empty, how can I help the person I am caring for? It is extremely important for carers to keep in mind their own well-being, as well as the well-being of the person with dementia.

Exactly this kind of situation arose one Friday. Sylvia's older son, Dave, who lives further away than his sister, Linda, had arranged to take Sylvia out for dinner at six o'clock in the evening. I had told Sylvia about it when we went through the day's events at the beginning of the day and mentioned her dinner date again straight after lunch. I immediately realised that this was a mistake. Sylvia's behaviour changed radically, as if she was possessed, and from that moment on she did not give me a second's peace.

She is pacing up and down in the living room, then she goes into her bedroom and lays her coat and cardigan out on the bed. Seconds later she is searching desperately for her handbag that is in its usual place in front of her on the armchair. She becomes very confused and agitated. She keeps swearing if she cannot find something immediately, but only she knows what it is she is looking for, and whatever she is looking for changes from second to second.

I know it is quite an event when your son is coming to take you out to dine and understand how she is feeling. I try everything I can think of to distract her or calm her down, but without success.

Then she starts directing her agitation at me, fussing about the plant that is missing from the table in the living room, claiming that I have moved it, although there has never been one there. She blames me for everything, calling me names, saying everything is wrong or not going the way she wants because of me. Yet everything is right around her; everything is as it has always been.

Anxiety is never a good thing for Sylvia and she looks as if she has really lost her wits. Every five minutes she wants to spend a penny. I am amazed by the energy she has. When, having just sat down following her last visit to the loo, she jumps up again straight away saying: 'I know what I have forgotten; a visit to the "House of Lords"!' and off she goes again, I feel I am losing my mind too.

I look at the clock on the wall. Only two o'clock. Four hours to go. I feel I cannot take this any longer; my non-existent ulcer is about to burst.

After only a moment's hesitation, a solution comes to mind and I take action: what possible harm can be done?

I let Sylvia know that I am going to my room for a minute to get something. On my way back, making sure I have Sylvia's attention, I stare at my mobile phone screen.

'Lucky I checked my phone!' I exclaim. 'I've just received a text message from Dave. He sends his apologies as he cannot make it tonight. He will take you out for dinner another day instead.'

I even pretend a little disappointment to support my act. What a performance!

In the next few seconds a miracle takes place. Sylvia relaxes; she lets out a big sigh from her tired body and then makes herself comfortable in her armchair as if she has blown out all her worries with this one breath. Total success! I know she is exhausted after a couple of hours of anxiety and intense activity. Twice she asks me to confirm that Dave is not coming, and when I do so the second time, she falls asleep right there in her armchair and lets the sandman take charge for the next hour.

I enjoy the quiet and take it as a reward. Even after Sylvia wakes up, I have no problems with her at all during the afternoon; everything goes like clockwork.

At a quarter to six, using the same ruse as earlier, I tell her that Dave can make it after all and will soon be here to take her out. These fifteen minutes give her just enough time to be physically and mentally prepared for his visit. She has no time for name-calling.

I do not believe I caused any harm by altering the truth. I would classify what I did as a white lie, which was essential in order for Sylvia and me to survive the afternoon. If a record player needle gets stuck in a groove on a vinyl record, someone needs to reach out, lift it up and then put it down again in an undamaged groove so that the record can continue playing. That is exactly how I feel when Sylvia's thoughts get stuck in a groove and she goes on and on about something until I step in and 'lift up the needle'.

■ ■ ■

Hiding things is another simple survival tool which can be seen as a variety of fibbing. The following incident happened exactly two years and two months after I first arrived at Sylvia's house.

As always when the post arrives, my lady opens it. One envelope includes a bright and attractive invitation to an annual event at the local church, a place she has not set foot in for at least fifteen years. Yet as soon as she reads the invitation, she is convinced that she goes there on a weekly basis. The date of the event is May 5. Today is April 3.

We have a calendar in the hall where we make a note of every significant event and appointment. I go with Sylvia to the calendar and help her to find the right day so that she can write in the event and the time it starts. We leave the invitation just under the calendar on top of the hall table, a place she passes 100 times a day.

One hour later I notice that she is desperately looking for something and talking to herself. At first I have no idea why as she cannot explain what is wrong. She continues to be very restless. Eventually she replies to my repeated questioning.

'I cannot find the thing that I must take with me tonight.'

Finally I get it: she is referring to the annual church event.

In a kindly voice I explain that the event is on in a month's time, so she has plenty of time to prepare 'the thing'. (She cannot verbalise what 'the thing' is and it does not seem to be the invitation itself.) She calms down for a while, we walk to the calendar together and double-check it. Looking at the note of the event on the calendar in her own handwriting is overwhelming evidence to her. She agrees to go back to the living room where I plan to distract her with something on TV.

However, soon after she sits down in her armchair, she stands up again, walks out of the room and returns in a few minutes, restless and anxious again. She keeps repeating she cannot find 'the thing' and that she needs it now as she is taking it with her tonight.

We go through exactly the same procedure that we went through only a few minutes before. Still patient as a saint, I listen to her grumbling and then I reorient her in time and today's date as we look at the calendar together.

After doing this for the fifth time, my mind is busy trying to find some way to solve this problem.

I decide to hide the invitation. It is so simple. I realise that every single time she passes the hall table, she catches sight of the invitation. When she is not looking, I go to the hall and put the invitation under a pile of papers so that it is not visible any more.

Sylvia does not mention 'the thing' again and I am confident that she will not mention it again until May 5.

Keeping in touch with family and friends plays a very important part in contributing to a carer's sense of well-being. My family and friends give me a lot of support whenever I can talk to them and focus on what they have to say – when Sylvia is with someone else or sleeping in her bedroom. Even listening to their problems gives my mind a rest as they are different topics from a different world. I cannot imagine how isolating and difficult – if not impossible – my job would have been before computers, the internet, Skype and social networking. I have friends and family living all around the globe who are very important to me and without whom I would be lost.

Chatting, complaining or just listening to them is part of my survival toolkit, as they offer a real distraction, a few minutes' holiday for my soul if you like. Then at night, after checking Sylvia is fast asleep, I often watch films and TV programmes, and listen to music on my computer, mostly movies, series and songs from my childhood or young adulthood. The familiar faces and voices from the past transport me back to a secure and happy time.

■ ■ ■

Of course, the dark days must not be ignored. As a carer, if you do not take enough care, depression can simply come uninvited and stay with you – it is easy to sink into it. There are always plenty of negative impacts on the life of a carer: days when the person with dementia is argumentative and agitated, or when visitors do or say things that make you feel bad; periods when just nothing seems to be right, colleagues put you down, you have a few sleepless nights; monotonous days with very limited conversations and a lack of appreciation. These are just a few of the numerous ways in which negativity can affect the carer and it can build up very quickly if you are not prepared for the assault. For instance, it took a while for me to realise that whereas Sylvia was enjoying visitors on a daily basis, meeting different people every day, going out and having set activities, all of which were giving a positive stimulus, helping with her mental state and preventing the occurrence of depression, I was not actively doing anything for my own enjoyment. Sometimes weeks would go by and chatting on Skype had been my only source of relaxation. Just a very few moments of personal enjoyment are all you need, which is why I took up running again. It is a lonely exercise, but it gives me some much-needed endorphins and I love the countryside round Sylvia's house. Every time I go for a run my batteries are recharged.

The other technique that helps to combat any dark days is to learn to observe all the many positives around you wherever you are and whatever you are doing. It can be the smallest thing, but it will help to get you through the bad periods.

In my case there are a number of things: just catching sight of my personal collection of music and films or looking out of the window at the surrounding fields and woods. Putting myself in the shoes of the person I am caring for always helps, but I have recently discovered a very useful variation on that technique: whenever I feel depression is looming, I look at myself through Sylvia's eyes and wonder what she thinks about me.

It is like a magic mirror on the scene. There is that someone who speaks in a strange accent, tells me what to do, comes into the bathroom when I am sitting on the loo, takes my clothes off, cannot make a decent cup of coffee, cooks boring food, puts things in the wrong place … The list is endless. If I play this 'reversing' game, I suddenly get myself back on course, become more empathetic, and feel I have the extra energy to carry on.

Along with all these ploys, whether you are a professional carer or a family member looking after someone with dementia, taking a complete break – not just snatching a bit of 'me time' – is essential. You must find the place and time when you can have some repose.

A carer's role consists of bearing an overwhelming weight made up of problems and tears, tasks and fears, guilt and sorrow. You therefore have to learn how to put these down from time to time. Sometimes a short break is enough to recharge your energy levels, but the time comes when the body indicates that a longer break is needed and only complete separation from the person or people who have the disease and from the place where you are living or working can ease your overloaded mind. Watch out for noticeable weight loss, changes in eating or sleeping habits, a constant feeling of exhaustion, when nothing can bring a smile to your face. These are signs you must obey: you must take a break.

■ ■ ■

CHAPTER
8

CARE HOME VERSUS IN-HOME CARE

When it comes to dementia, people are clearly divided about which form of care is more beneficial to someone affected by the condition: institutional care or the home environment.

My view is that people should be able to choose, although in some cases the decision has to be based on the financial circumstances of the person in need of care and families have no choice about which they think might be better for their loved one. I am fortunate to have had experience of both forms of care, as I worked in care homes for several years before becoming a live-in carer in the home of someone who lives with dementia.

If someone were to ask me which I would prefer if I myself had dementia, at the moment I would be inclined to choose my own house. If I were physically capable of staying at home, I imagine it would be a nice feeling to know that there was someone living with me and looking after me as a guardian, making sure I had everything I needed, keeping me company but still giving me some sort of independence, however small. I would like to be able to retain my freedom to make decisions, something which automatically comes with the title, 'lady of the house'.

As I have already emphasised, person-centred care is the basis of good dementia care, but it is almost impossible for even the very best care homes to truly follow this approach.

I know from my own experience that unfortunately many of the care homes I used to work for are short-staffed a lot of the time and workers come and go, so there are not many people who represent a 'familiar face' to dementia residents. The carers on duty can be overloaded with tasks that would be enough to fill a double shift and they are only able to spend a few minutes with each resident on the essentials: dispensing pills, quickly completing any personal care necessary and serving food. Many residents are left alone again for hours. Doctors rarely see the few residents assigned to them and often fill out prescriptions automatically on the advice of a carer; they are in a rush along with everyone else – the admin staff, the kitchen staff, the cleaners. The result is depressing. Lacking even a few friendly words, never being asked how they really are or if they need anything, after a short while many residents just give up on the basic human need for interaction.

According to statistics, the average life expectancy after being admitted into a care home is 18 months. Of course, there are people who live a great deal longer after admission, but sadly there are also those whose stay is even shorter.

Naturally, the causes of death vary, but there are two illnesses that I came across a lot during the time I worked in care homes. The number of people suffering from a urinary tract infection (UTI) was significantly high and can be related to lack of movement or mobility, low levels of hygiene, dehydration, inadequate use of the lavatory or bathing facilities that are a potential source of infection. Depression was also extremely common, but was often ignored and unrecognised. Severe depression can result in psychosomatic symptoms, which can damage the immune system, leaving elderly people particularly vulnerable to viruses and bacteria.

■ ■ ■

As the number of people diagnosed with dementia continues to increase dramatically around the world, fortunately more and more initiatives are being taken to create dementia-friendly environments in care homes, respite homes and hospitals. Those responsible for care facilities have started to recognise the need for something different, something that contributes a little 'magic touch' so that those with the disease can feel safe and comfortable.

I am not talking about luxurious facilities requiring millions of pounds in investment. Keeping only to a very modest budget, I have seen care homes successfully adjust their facilities so that they can provide care that is more specific to the particular needs of people with dementia, including interior design that supports and stimulates people living with the condition.

Many of the ideas used in care homes specialising in dementia care can easily be used or adapted successfully for in-home care too.

First, colour. Colour stimulates the brain and is useful as a pointer. Neutral-coloured walls and paintwork are the norm in many care homes,and in people's homes, but people suffering from short-term memory loss and disorientation in time and location need contrasts to guide them. Doors painted different colours help people with this mental condition to find the room they are looking for and signs on the doors reinforce the use of colour.

Research has shown that the majority of people with dementia who are literate retain their ability to read until the final stages of the disease. In a dementia-friendly environment, everything is labelled – the remote, each kitchen cupboard, the wardrobe, the drawers in the chest of drawers

– so that the people with this condition are constantly given the support they need to help them find the remote control for the TV, the mugs, the coffee, the cardigans and the socks that they are looking for.

One of the main aims of dementia care in both an institutional setting and in the home environment is to retain people's independence in terms of doing everyday tasks and to 'stretch' it as far as if possible within the bounds of safety. Care home staff specially trained in dementia care are more like family members or friends caring for a person with dementia. They do not do everything for the residents, they do not patronise them, and the care they give is unobtrusive. If people who have dementia feel that they are useful, their self-esteem is stronger and they believe in themselves more. Their risk of developing depression is therefore lower. Besides, it gives them great pleasure and keeps them busy if they are able to change channels on the TV or make a cup of coffee.

Every ornament and object has a function in a dementia-friendly environment in a care home or a person's home. I have witnessed many positive changes in the behaviour of a person with dementia living at home after small modifications have been made around the house based on ideas that stimulate people with this disease. The coloured bubbles of a lava lamp in the living room, a fish tank, a noticeboard full of photos, interesting objects hanging on the wall, the daily paper always available on the side table, a clock that shows the time and the day of the week, cushions in different shapes and sizes on the sofa providing a choice of cushions to lean against and cushions to hug – these are just a very few examples of things that support the well-being of people with this mental condition.

In many care home facilities, residents can furnish their room with their own familiar pieces of furniture as well as being allowed to bring in items such as family photos, personal ornaments, handmade blankets and toys. These objects all tell stories and encourage people with dementia to talk about their past, as long as there are members of staff or visitors who are interested and have time to listen.

At home, some people like watching TV from an armchair, some prefer straight-backed chairs and others like to have their feet up on the sofa. All these options are available in a dementia-friendly care home, where all the furniture is subject to very careful selection. In a care home designed for people with the disease, a wide range of different heights, colours and textures in sofas, beds, tables, wardrobes and chests of drawers are provided that, despite their differences, form a harmonious whole.

In the same way that the home of a person with this mental condition can use ideas from a dementia-friendly environment, the aim of a dementia-friendly care home is to create a homelike environment, where every resident will find something to help them establish their daily routine in a place that feels like home.

■ ■ ■

It has already been mentioned that a golden rule in dementia care is that those with the condition can do whatever they want, even if what they want to do seems irrational, as long as it is safe for them and for others, taking into consideration their physical abilities, well-being and mental state.

Due to their lack of judgement and their lack of any sense of danger, people with this disease need constant attention and monitoring as well as time and patience, which is why it is impossible to provide this kind of care in a non-dementia-specific facility, especially in hospitals. Staff simply have no time to monitor people with dementia closely and are unable to use the time-consuming techniques necessary to rebalance any upsets in the resident or patient's mental state. The results can be catastrophic. What a resident or patient experiences in a non-dementia-friendly institution is exactly the opposite of what would calm them down, the opposite of what to them indicates safety, stability and tranquillity. In such places, people can become totally out of control unless medicated, and a vicious circle begins. Staff are under pressure, they do not even have a minimal understanding of the condition, so they give residents or patients negative labels. It is very distressing to overhear comments such as: 'Where has that lunatic disappeared to again? I don't believe it,' or 'Look at that nutcase, he hasn't touched his meal. He doesn't even know what a knife and fork are for.'

The latter comment could have been used to refer to a particular resident in a care home I once worked in, but luckily it was a dementia-friendly environment.

I am sitting at the dining table when I notice that one of the residents on my table has not touched his food. I know he has not had anything to eat since breakfast apart from a biscuit. I ask him what is wrong. The answer is, 'Nothing.' I ask if he has any pain. The answer is, 'No.' All of his non-verbal communication indicates that he is happy to be there and he smiles as he smells the delicious odours floating up to his nose from the soup plate. I have absolutely no idea why he is not eating.

I decide to try something. I put my spoon down in its starting place beside my plate. Then I use one of the most effective ways there is to get someone's full attention: the smile. If you keep smiling at someone, the other person will almost always smile back.

As soon as I have his attention, I pick my spoon up very

slowly from the right side of the plate. With a careful, deliberate movement I dip it into the soup and then lift the spoon to my mouth, all the while smiling and keeping constant eye contact. I use exaggerated mime to show how delicious the soup is as I swallow.

Slowly he looks down at his plate, and with my next spoonful he starts to copy me. It is impossible to express just what a wonderful feeling it is to be able to jump-start his memory and get his 'engine' started. By the time I take my third spoonful we are eating in time with each other, our movements synchronised – his ability to eat with a spoon has become automatic again.

I realise that his mind is overloaded by too much information from the table setting and confused by all the different cutlery. At suppertime I am very careful with the table setting and just give him the cutlery he needs for each course as it arrives. He has no problem in eating.

■ ■ ■

Before I came to look after Sylvia, the family did try moving her into a care home for a trial period, but the result was a total failure. Her family thought the care home would provide Sylvia with company and a safe home, but it very quickly became apparent that she could not cope with an institutional environment where the world did not revolve around her and she was not the one in charge. Her aggressive and increasingly challenging behaviour evoked a very negative response from the already overworked staff, who did not have time to sit down and talk to her. The carers only made contact with her when it was absolutely necessary, when they gave her her pills, for instance; otherwise they stayed away from her. Naturally, this situation led to that vicious cycle where only Sylvia's basic needs were catered for – any other needs were ignored together with her feelings, which meant that she started to lose what remaining control she had over her mood and social behaviour. Her bitterness and frustration were expressed in ways that the staff later described as 'putting herself and others in danger'. She started to throw her medication at the carers, she wiped her faeces on the furniture around her, she went in and out of other residents' rooms during her night wanderings and she shouted at just about everybody.

The time soon came when the family was notified of the difficulties Sylvia was causing and, very politely but firmly, the care home informed them that they could not keep her there any longer. The family had hoped that she would be given the time to adapt to her new home, but she was not given the opportunity to function as a human being there so was unable to adapt.

After looking again at all the options available, Sylvia's relatives decided on an in-home care option that did not cost significantly more than a room and 24-hour care in a dementia-friendly care home. The one-to-one lifestyle in the familiar environment of her own home surrounded by lovely memories immediately worked much better for her and as a result her excessive behaviours were reduced drastically. It was very clear as soon as I arrived that she was the lady of the house and that anyone who came to support her daily living came only as a guest and visitor.

Whether a person with dementia is being cared for at home or in a dementia-friendly facility, there are four 'foundation stones' that apply in absolutely every case: patience, time, attention, observation.

Extreme patience is needed in order to deal with all the many facets of the condition and every small detail needs to be taken into account, especially when it comes to a challenging phase.

Carers must take time to carefully analyse their responses in different situations, so that they communicate with the person with the disease in a variety of ways. The affected brain is simply not able to keep up with the normal rates of information processing and cannot even make a very simple choice. Sooner or later the solution will come as to how to deal with a situation; all carers need to do is to wait and to listen to the answer when it does arrive.

When proper attention is paid to people with this condition the result is always positive. They will open up if they feel someone really cares about what they think, what they wish for or what they would like to say. Ignoring their needs is one of the main causes of their frustration and agitation. Paying genuine attention where it is needed and showing that you truly care will always save time in the long run.

Finally, observation is an invaluable tool that supports care work and makes it more effective. Daily observation gives carers the chance to find logic in the illogical, so that responses can be more flexible and the best result can be found for a particular problem. It also provides useful data, which, after a while, can be used to measure the dynamics, the tendency and the progress of certain behaviour elements within the condition.

I call observation 'a bit of awareness in the unrealistic world of dementia'.

CHAPTER
9

THE 'MUST NOT DO' LIST

I have had the privilege of meeting and caring for hundreds of people living with dementia. I have had personal experience of many of the different types, including mixed dementia, where more than one type of dementia affects the brain (I talked about this in chapter 6), and of all the different stages of the condition. The care needs of every single individual with this disease are unique, with different techniques and approaches required in order to keep the person's behaviour under control.

The importance of learning and knowledge therefore cannot be emphasised enough, but a carer also needs a special skill in order to find the way into the heart of a person with dementia: a willingness to tune in to another person's wavelength, coupled with very sound common sense.

As well as making sure that I follow the positive basic rules already mentioned, I find it helpful to bear in mind a list of things that I must *not* do, however tempted I might be.

When a person with dementia shouts, becomes aggressive and agitated, it is easy to take things personally and follow suit, especially if you are tired, but you must not raise your voice and must not give any hint of aggression or agitation.

When I was still getting to know Sylvia and finding my feet as her carer I found it difficult to tolerate her compulsive packing and unpacking of her handbag and wanted to break the routine. She has several pairs of reading glasses, but she only likes one particular pair, which she usually keeps in her handbag. On the shelf next to her armchair are two other pairs in their cases, just in case she wants them.

Sylvia tries on one of the pairs of glasses from the shelf.

'I can't see anything through these glasses,' she seethes and picks up her handbag from the floor beside her armchair. She opens it up, takes everything out and puts it on the coffee table next to her. Different compartments are unzipped and emptied, every coin is taken out of her purse and counted. All the time she is commenting on her actions.

She then starts to put everything back. It is obvious that she has forgotten what she is looking for. Slowly each item is replaced in the handbag and zips are zipped up. Her work complete, she puts her handbag down on the floor, next to her armchair.

She reaches out for the newspaper. Then she heaves a big sigh.

'I can't start reading the paper without my glasses. Where can they be?'

The same routine starts all over again with the same running commentary: she puts the handbag on her lap, takes every single item out, forgets the original reason for searching, puts everything back, closes up the handbag, returns it to the floor and reaches out for the paper again.

If I do not break this compulsive repetition, she might never stop packing and unpacking. I try to suggest where she might look.

'What about looking in that other case on the shelf?'

'Don't tell me what to do. I am not a child; I used to be in the army. I do not need your help,' she retorts.

She begins her search again. I decide to take matters into my own hands and pick up the other case on the shelf. The pair she is looking for might be hiding in there.

She suddenly snaps at me, 'Just where do you think you're taking that box?'

I have had enough. I raise my voice. 'I'm not taking your box anywhere. Do you think I need your box? I was just looking for your glasses so you could read the paper.'

She shouts at me, 'Oh, just leave me alone, will you? My glasses are not lost. What are you talking about?'

On this occasion losing my patience caused the situation to spiral out of control and Sylvia became very confused and agitated. Only by repressing my anger deep down, using my calmest tone of voice and the best diversionary tactic I could think of did I manage to retrieve the situation. When Sylvia wasn't looking, I found her favourite reading glasses in a side pocket in her handbag immediately.

I soon realised that it was the search and the commentary that were important in Sylvia's handbag packing and unpacking routine, not finding the glasses. By paying attention to the commentary that accompanied Sylvia's search and adding in my own comments wondering where the glasses could possibly be, I became part of the game and added to the feeling of comfort that the routine gave her.

People with dementia always respond to a calm but firm voice as it shows that carers know how to take control of the situation and what they are doing. No matter how stubborn and unyielding she may be sometimes, I know that Sylvia likes it when I am definite when necessary, as it makes her feel safe and in good hands. Everyone, whether they have the disease or not, is reassured by the message 'Everything will be just fine.' Maintaining friendly eye contact while using a gentle tone of voice adds to the calming process, but be careful not to fix a person with dementia with your gaze. No one likes to be stared at.

Do not make people with this condition feel that you are against them, but constantly make it clear that you are on their side. On days when Sylvia's behaviour is more challenging than usual, I am very aware and alert, not only in my actions, but verbally too. I keep explaining why I am there, what the benefits are of having another person on her side and of using their assistance when needed.

Never ridicule someone with dementia by mentioning their disability. Do not laugh at them, and be careful with teasing. Remember that even affectionate leg pulling can be humiliating if the joke is too complicated for them to understand.

Sarcasm is an unfair and unkind tool to use against these people. I know a tendency to be sarcastic is one of my worst features and it was something I used to ease my inner tension when I first started to work with people with dementia and which, I am ashamed to admit, surfaced again involuntarily in my first few days of looking after Sylvia. Whenever a sarcastic comment is on the tip of my tongue, I call to mind a clear picture of Sylvia withdrawing sadly and quietly to her room as a result of my overt sarcasm.

The technique that works again and again in so many situations is diversion. Once you have dealt with the immediate issue or problem that the person you are caring for is experiencing, diversion is almost always a highly effective course of action, especially if you offer a simple choice. Continuing to concentrate on the problem always makes it worse.

A recurring problem that Sylvia has, especially during winter, is nosebleeds. They are not the result of any physical impact or stress, but are most likely caused by a combination of dry and cold air irritating her aged mucous membranes. She tends to get hysterical when it happens because she is frightened by the sight of blood on her hanky and becomes more and more anxious, causing the bleeding to increase. I have to bear all the 'must nots' in mind when I deal with this kind of incident and guide Sylvia back to her own reality.

'Call my daughter at once; ask her to come over immediately and tell her we have a huge problem!' she shrieks while bursting into tears and going into a panic attack. 'Do something, you idiot!'

I ignore the insult and decide to put my nursing training into immediate action. I look her gently in the eye and speak calmly but firmly.

'I am a qualified nurse and I know exactly what to do. There's nothing to worry about.'

As I start to act quickly and decisively, she feels that she is in good hands. I get her full attention and instruct her to keep some pressure on her nose by pinching it. As soon as she focuses on the task, I can sense that she is beginning to let her anxiety go.

I encourage her to tell me how she is feeling. While she is talking to me, I am actively listening. If nothing else, I utter an

'Aha' or 'I see' as feedback so that she knows I am there and that I am listening. As well as my confident tone of voice, the questions I ask, and the active listening, I make sure that I agree with at least some of what she says. Even when she says something totally illogical or ridiculous, I still find something in her remark that I can agree to with comments such as 'Yes, I know' or 'You're perfectly right.' These reactions make it clear to her that I am on her side, we are in the same team, and, like magic, her hysteria and confusion decrease. Gradually she forgets to cry and her breathing returns to a normal, steady rate.

When the bleeding has stopped I give Sylvia the choice of staying in her bathroom where it is less comfortable or going into the living room where she can watch her favourite Poirot *episode.*

'Which one would you prefer?' I ask.

It is obvious that all the free capacity of her emotionally overloaded mind becomes fully occupied in trying to find an answer to my question, and all her previous concerns about her nosebleed vanish.

Fifteen minutes after her nosebleed began, Sylvia is sitting in her comfy armchair, sipping her tea and is fully engaged in trying to follow every move of Monsieur Poirot. Her mind has already deleted all memory of the incident.

When their mood changes for the worse and problems of regulation of feelings emerge, people with dementia are prone to more confusion than usual and it is important find a way of guiding them back to their own reality.

A key item on the carer's 'must not do' list is never to show fear or anxiety. If a confused person with this mental condition is in trouble and their carer lacks self-confidence, panics and is unable to cope, tension can easily be increased.

Do not invade the personal space of a person with this disease. Everyone feels uncomfortable or threatened if someone gets too close. All physical contact is best avoided in situations of challenging behaviour, because it can easily be misunderstood by someone in an overheated state of mind. People living with dementia lack reliable judgement, therefore certain sudden movements, touches or gestures towards them can be interpreted as an instant threat and their reaction can be an impulsive attack, especially if someone approaches them unseen and unexpected from behind.

People with dementia do not intend to hurt their carers, except if they feel threatened or attacked. Confrontation in these cases never does any good and can easily lead to a more serious situation where they become even more stressed, confused and aggressive as a consequence of the negative response to their behaviour. Their challenging behaviour will continue until the original trigger that fuelled it is found, resolved or removed: there is always a reason why people with this condition are aggressive.

Physical restraint or curtailment of freedom are not permitted and carers must be aware of the danger of depriving people with dementia of their liberty or abusing them. Of course, having bedrails up is acceptable if it is in the care plan and necessary as a safety tool for the prevention of falls, but there are less obvious forms of deprivation of liberty or abuse which can happen on a daily basis, and some of these actions are in the same technical category as tying people up against their will.

If Sylvia wants to go to a place we can only get to by taking the car and I am not in the mood to go anywhere, I could say: 'Let's stay in the house instead. You can go out to the garden if you need some fresh air.' This is a very simple demonstration of abusing someone by acting against their will. My possible response may seem 100 per cent innocent, but I am refusing to do something I could do to meet Sylvia's needs so would be guilty of deprivation of liberty in my care in a court of law.

Those living with dementia have difficulties in expressing themselves, and carers should never do anything against the will of the people in their care, unless it would risk their or others' safety. Forcing people with this mental condition to do something they do not want to do guarantees a fiasco every time.

■ ■ ■

With experience, aggressive episodes can be defused or blocked, and imminent aggressive episodes can be detected and, in some cases, prevented from happening. Obviously, not all the triggers involved, for instance changes in the weather or the side effects of medication, can be avoided, but by giving time, patience and attention to the person with dementia, carers can identify several precursors that can indicate that negative changes in behaviour are about to happen.

Aimless wandering, making unusual noises, suddenly becoming demanding, getting agitated – basically, any minor, out of the ordinary behaviour change shows that a storm is on the way, just as the air gets filled with a spicy smell before a real thunderstorm, the air pressure increases and threatening dark clouds obscure the sun.

During aggressive episodes, carers must be prepared for people with dementia swearing, shouting, kicking, punching, spitting, damaging objects or even themselves, and have the 'level of skill required to care for somebody who is as likely to hit you as welcome you'.[5]

Everyone has an innate 'danger alarm' which can give rise to aggression and it is worth always keeping in mind a few of the wide range of causes that can underlie aggressive behaviour: confusion, fear, a defensive reaction to the threat of intrusion into a person's personal space, failure of competence, reality confrontation, misunderstanding events, attention-seeking, overreaction, psychosis, delusional ideation.

At the beginning of the 'carer and person-with-dementia' relationship it can be extremely difficult and frustrating for people with dementia to accept that, having been independent up to that point, they now need constant assistance with simple, everyday tasks. They still want to feel that they are the 'boss', but they have to have a helper on hand to assist them not only with general tasks, but also with their most intimate daily routines. Not surprisingly, this can lead to unusual behaviour or aggression in many people.

I remember there was a nasty crack on Sylvia's bottom due to her poor hygiene and an infection she had contracted several months before I came into her life. It was so advanced that you could see the inner tissues in the open wound. This was located on a delicate body part where germs and dirt could enter freely from whatever was around the anus. Giving a shower was a daily task requiring the utmost patience and empathy. Sylvia had to trust me perfectly from the time she first uncovered her body in front of me and stepped into the shower where I would use various items of equipment to make sure she started the day fresh and clean while protecting her dignity. Then dried, but still half naked, I managed to persuade her to lie on her bed.

I had to be extremely careful with the next stage. With one wrongly chosen action or by rushing her, the whole routine would have failed as I knew she could not be forced to do anything against her will.

By using a soft, kind, step-by-step approach I got her to lie on her back first, and then to roll over onto her side giving me free access to one of her most intimate body parts so that I could apply ointment to her skin.

Three months after I took over Sylvia's care, her skin had healed thanks to the combination of properly maintained hygiene and the ointment prescribed by the doctor.

■ ■ ■

Fear of failure is a common trigger for aggression or challenging behaviour. When dealing with people living with dementia it is wise to remember the importance of asking simple questions and giving simple instructions.

Visitors who are not sensitive to Sylvia's condition sometimes bombard her with a mass of information and questions. Her brain automatically switches off, her body language sends out the very clear message 'I am not interested' and she turns her face vacantly away from her visitor. Her defensive reaction to her fear of failing in social interaction is to choose to stop all communication.

Reducing the options to two is an excellent example of good practice. This stimulates the peron with dementia, engages his or her attention and encourages him or her to make a simple decision. It is as simple as: 'What would you like to have with your tea, some chocolate or a biscuit?'

'Chocolate, please. Thank you, darling.'

Confrontation with reality is a problem for Sylvia as far as her age is concerned as she is convinced that she is 57 years old. Whenever she is asked how old she is, by doctors or by other people, this is always the answer she gives. In these instances, I quietly give the true figure if necessary, but mostly it is absolutely unnecessary to confront her with reality, for two reasons. First, her real age is totally irrelevant to her everyday life and, second, it upsets her very badly when she does realise her age.

Shortly after my arrival, it was the week of Sylvia's 90th birthday and it was extremely hard to avoid the subject. When it was only the two of us, I simply chose not to talk about it, but she kept having visits from friends and family members and, understandably, an increased number of greeting cards arrived. One particular birthday card had an enormous '90' shouting the truth into Sylvia's face. As she read it and realised that all her cards were to congratulate her on her 90th birthday, she went through a terrible trauma. She ended up in tears most of that week and her behaviour became much more negative and challenging than usual.

'Somebody, please tell me, if I am really that old, why am I still alive? I should have died a long time ago,' she said, sobbing. I felt terrible and as soon as I could I hid the card with the huge number on it and any other cards that mentioned her real age, in order to reduce her distress.

Adaptive paranoia is another 'frequent visitor' to the lives of people with dementia. Most carers have experience of this problem and are blamed for stealing money or objects, for moving something the person with dementia believes belongs somewhere else or spiriting away something that exists only in the cared-for's mind, or for mistakes the person with dementia has made him or herself.

I will never forget the day when I saw Sylvia looking through the post in the hall.

I notice that Sylvia has a pen in her hand and that she is making notes on one of the envelopes.

A few minutes later, I walk past her in the hall on my way to the bathroom. It is clear she is having difficulty in reading her own handwriting. She asks for my help.

'I can't read my own writing. What does this say?'

'Let's see. I'm sure you can read your own handwriting better than I can. Why don't we work it out together?'

103

She immediately blows her top and starts shouting at me: 'This is not my handwriting! Do you think I'm so stupid that if I wrote this I wouldn't be able to read it! I am not an idiot! This is awful handwriting! It's terrible!'

She bawls me out completely. It is essential for me to remain calm.

'Of course you're not stupid. This is dreadful writing. Shall I have a look?'

I pretend to try to understand what is written on the envelope.

'How on earth could anybody have such cramped handwriting as this?' I ask her. 'Whoever wrote it, has given us a very difficult decoding task!'

Sylvia nods vigorously, in absolute agreement.

'Let's ask Linda when she comes,' I add. 'She's the one who deals with all your official correspondence.'

'Oh, yes. She'll sort this out, I'm sure,' is Sylvia's reply and she releases all her worry in one deep sigh. A minute later it is all forgotten.

Carers must not forget that people with dementia do forget.

■ ■ ■

CHAPTER
10

THERE IS ALWAYS SOMEONE BEHIND DEMENTIA

There is a personality in every single human being, an absolutely unique code and pattern built up over a lifetime, and the way to understanding the person hidden behind the condition of dementia must not be blocked by obstacles such as language differences, communication problems, short-term memory loss or other physical and mental causes. This is the fundamental aim of the person-centred care model I have always used – to help overcome these obstacles while finding out what the person with dementia really needs and what he or she really wants. That is why the person must be taken into account first, before the disease.

I cannot emphasise too strongly the importance of the person-centred approach in dementia care. Taking each affected person as an individual, carers must start to learn their life history, habits, hobbies, fears, things they are proud of and all the tiny elements that make them happy or sad. They must get to know the subjective world of dementia, the world of the forever 'I don't know'. Carers must try to make contact with the personality that is hidden behind the barricades and search for an indirect connection while constantly checking on the physical needs of each person in their care, ensuring their comfort and doing their best to make them feel at home and safe. It is not good enough only to hear what people with dementia say; carers must let the words reach their innermost minds, if not their souls, if they really want to understand what the person with dementia is trying to communicate.

Efforts to make a connection with a person with this condition will be much more effective if these guiding principles are kept in mind. In this way, carers can build up a kind of 'special manual' that quickly provides the answers to questions about the whys of seemingly odd or annoying behaviour patterns.

If somebody desperately wants to go 'home', insisting that where they are is not the place where they belong, such behaviour can be understood as communicating the fact that they do not feel safe or comfortable at that moment for a variety of reasons, and that they want to go somewhere where they will feel reassured.

If the individual keeps saying they must go to work, even though they have been retired for years, it can mean they yearn to be useful and busy again, and are feeling bored, worthless and useless.

If a person with dementia is looking for a wife or husband who died years earlier, it might highlight an individual's lack of company and need for emotional support.

Speaking this unique 'language' helps carers not only to understand different situations but means that they can also be the rock on which these people can rely and trust.

During my time working with Sylvia, I have noticed that it has become an involuntary habit of mine to speak to her more slowly and with more articulation than I usually do with other people. She speaks clearly and deliberately, perhaps because of her background in languages, and at first I think I copied her, which incidentally was very good for my English. Now, I believe that my speaking slowly has the added benefit of giving her the chance to think during the conversation and the time to find and select the right words to express as clearly as possible what she really means or wants to say. I also always take care to eliminate every possible barrier or extraneous noise from our verbal connection.

When Sylvia is watching TV, she usually has the volume up high because of her hearing impairment. Although she has got hearing aids, she prefers not to wear them at home, especially when she is watching television, as they make not only the speech but also the background noise far too loud. Naturally there are moments when she wants to say something during a *Poirot* or *Miss Marple* episode, and I always automatically turn the volume down immediately to get rid of a very disturbing communication barrier.

In verbal communication I have learnt never to switch topics quickly as people with dementia are unable to follow quick changes of idea. If I have asked a question and I realise that Sylvia's response has nothing to do with the question asked, or she says something totally incoherent, I try to rephrase what I have just asked or said, and that usually solves the problem.

It is part of my morning routine with Sylvia to look at photos of her family and friends on the noticeboard next to the kitchen table. Then I not only use words, but also point out the person we are talking about. The double effect of verbal and visual information gives extra cognitive support, and helps avoid any misunderstanding. I always enjoy our chats about the photos. It is a great tool for a daily assessment of my dear Sylvia's memory and current mental state, and it is an important part of my daily report as it really helps me to see any improvement or deterioration in her condition through her ability to recognise people who are close to her. There is a selection of current and old photos of close friends and family members, as well as visitors like Jeanne who keep her company on certain days of the week when they take her out for a walk or a coffee.

There are days now, getting on for three years after I first got to know Sylvia, when she is unable to recognise even her own younger son. Unlike Dave, her older son, he lives abroad so she does not often see him. On other days, Sylvia easily identifies everyone in the photos by name. Naturally, if she is ill or tired, I do not force this daily 'game'. When she has difficulty recognising people in the pictures, I know I have to take things slowly, so I use very simple topics in conversation, simple sentences or questions, giving her brain a 'day off', so to speak.

To begin with it is very hard for someone with a clear sense of logic to put up with thousands of minor actions, words or thoughts that could easily drive anybody crazy. From the very first moment carers step through the door into the world of dementia, their own worlds are turned upside down. I still have to remind myself constantly: do not correct Sylvia's actions, do not guide her in the direction I think is better for her. Constant correction increases the impact of negativity and can have the effect – a high risk in a person with a mental conditon – of provoking reactions of aggression and/or agitation.

Sylvia not only likes searching for her glasses, she likes everything about them: putting them on, taking them off, cleaning them, getting them out from their cases or putting them away, even nagging and praising them. She is particularly fond of her sunglasses and can often spend all the daylight hours on a dark winter's day shuffling about the house wearing them.

One cloudy day I made the mistake of not keeping quiet when I noticed that she was about to put her sunglasses on to read the newspaper.

'I wonder if it would be better to use your reading glasses,' I dare to remark. 'I think sunglasses make the page look darker.'

Sylvia puts her sunglasses on carefully and starts reading.

'I can see perfectly well,' she retorts. She stubbornly carries on reading, determined to demonstrate that the sunglasses are just right for the purpose she wants them for, and that she has chosen and put on the sunglasses for good reason.

'Oh, good,' I reply, keen not to continue the confrontation. There is no point in arguing. I decide to go out of the room. It has to be her choice to take off the sunglasses, not mine.

By the time I come back into the living room, the sunglasses are no longer in evidence and the paper is on the coffee table. I brace myself as she reaches for her handbag.

The techniques of validation and reminiscence are two elementary constituents of the caring approach in which the person takes precedence over his or her dementia.

The validation technique was developed by Naomi Feil[6,7] and a video showing her with Gladys Wilson, a lady in the advanced stages of the disease, is often shown on dementia training courses and can be seen on Youtube.[8] This video effectively demonstrates the essence of validation, not to mention the success and popularity of the presenter. The point of this approach is that the opinions of the person with dementia are acknowledged, respected, heard, and, regardless of whether or not the listener actually agrees with them, treated with genuine respect as a legitimate expression of their feelings, rather than marginalised or dismissed. From a carer's point of view, the validation technique is about acceptance and guidance as a result of constant and close attention which involves picking up on little hints. The carer acknowledges the world of the person with dementia, their beliefs, their reality, and then enters their world, letting them take the lead. This approach demands lots of patience, kindness and smiles and a high level of awareness.

I used to show the video of Naomi Feil with Gladys Wilson to my team when I was the leader of a dementia-specific facility. It is very useful to see how the technique works in practice and the viewer is left in tears at the end. It shows Naomi Feil achieving a significant communication breakthrough with Gladys, who up until that point had been quite mute. With Naomi Feil's encouragement, Gladys finishes the session by joining in with singing a hymn and this could only have come about by someone giving her enough time to emerge from her isolated and, until then, very closed world. Naomi Feil achieved this first by hoping that Gladys would reciprocate smiling with a smile, then by demonstrating how she reacted to the slow, gentle stroking of her fingers on Gladys' cheeks, before finally using Gladys' memory of familiar hymns and her strong religious belief. The result is breath-taking. Gladys joins in with the rhythm of the hymn, taps in time to the tune, then mouths the lyrics in a while, until finally the previously mute lady with advanced dementia is singing.

Validation is not the same as lying. I would never lie to a person with dementia about important things, but use the technique of validation successfully on a daily basis.

The fact that Sylvia uses the present tense when she talks about her mother and father no longer surprises me, but as her condition deteriorates, I notice that she is putting more and more twists and turns into her stories about her parents. Increasingly, her broken and confused memories mean that she is taking on her mother's life history and career path and believes that she has a successful career on the stage. The condition of dementia distorts memories and often integrates into the person's own life story events from the past that did not necessarily happen to them, but to family members or friends. Sylvia is turning more and more memories into her reality and confidently talks about events as if they had happened to her and were her own experiences.

Sylvia looks at me with her serious, anxious look.

'It is very cold out there, my dear, so I don't think that I can go on stage tomorrow. Could you call and tell them, as they might need to cancel the performance? I feel bad about it as I know the audience will be disappointed, but look at me, I can hardly get out of this armchair.'

I summon up all my knowledge on the topic, but I know that I cannot agree to Sylvia's request. Validation is what is needed. I trust my instincts to guide my reaction, as I do most of the time during my care work:

'I don't know about the play, but in weather like this, people don't usually choose to go out to the theatre,' I say without any word of a lie.

'You might be right, dear. Do you think I should call them?'

The power of the false reality may be weakening, but it is still there.

'I tell you what. Why don't we go to the kitchen? I'll put the kettle on and we can have a nice cup of tea, then I'm sure we'll work out what to do. What do you think?'

My actions immediately mirror my words. I jump up from my comfy armchair, full of energy, put a cheerful smile on my face, walk to the kitchen and put the kettle on. Sylvia follows me into the kitchen.

I take the tea back into the living room and Sylvia comes with me. I quickly turn the TV on and thanks to the fast-

changing pictures of the news, Sylvia's mind is completely freed of the stubborn, false memories.

Reminiscence therapy is a crucial part of dementia care work. This person-centred approach concentrates on the personal life history and the most pleasant memories and occasions of the life of a person with the condition. Recalling personal experiences and skills that the person used to have, while showing a lot of love and interest, provides very strong support to the current mental state so that the mind can function at its maximum. If a person's mental and emotional states are well balanced, they have a positive effect on the person's physical health too.

Webster's Reminiscence Functions Scale (RFS)[9] gives eight reasons why people reminisce: boredom reduction, bitterness revival, preparation for death, conversation, identity, intimacy maintenance, problem-solving, and to teach/inform.

Psychologists use reminiscence therapeutically to improve coping skills. Although the effectiveness of this therapy has been debated, the therapy appears to have positive and lasting results for elderly people. I do not have the detailed medical or scientific knowledge to join in the debate, but there is no doubt that recalling positive memories plays an important part in maintaining the mental equilibrium of people with dementia.

Dozens of studies and research projects have quantified the effectiveness of reminiscence. For instance, positive changes in mood have been recorded using the Cornell Scale for Depression in Dementia (CSDD), a scale used to measure the level of depression of people living with the disease, and improved scores have been documented using the Mini-Mental State Examination (MMSE), which measures cognitive impairment.

When I use reminiscence to recall positive times, I always find that the mood and emotional state of the person with dementia improve instantly and that this therapy has a 'healing' effect even in sadder moments or on more challenging days. Cognitive functions run more smoothly as a result, although reminiscence has to be used over and over again as the improvement is not steady or long-lasting.

When Sylvia is overcome by depression or other upsetting feelings, I use several positive memories that help her slip back into the right emotional state. She always gladly talks about her parents, and it is interesting that they remain more powerfully in her broken mind than her husband, who she hardly ever mentions. Talking about her mother's roles as an actress never fails to bring a smile to her face, her frown lines relax and her appearance brightens up instantly. The same happens when Sylvia takes a virtual tour of her school years. She often says that she would love to go back to school again to learn something new and exciting, and she repeats again and again how much she loved to see her teacher standing on the dais with fingers covered in powdery chalk pointing at the board.

Another reminiscence that eases her troubled mind is when she recalls the time she worked as a designer at one of the largest fashion houses in England, when her taste, opinion and flair mattered to others. She is still interested in fashion and loves commenting on different outfits and accessories when we are watching a film or when she sees pictures in the paper. 'Look, my dear, how awful that bow looks on that adorable royal blue jacket! How could anyone make such a mess of something like that?' she fumes.

A wide array of tools supports reminiscence. Sylvia and I often listen to music on the radio, and I constantly observe her reactions, facial expressions and body language as she listens. I can tell in a moment if she likes something or not, and know which songs, lyrics and melodies, particularly from her childhood and early adulthood, have a positive effect on helping happy memories to surface. If they do, Sylvia starts one of her endless stories and becomes chatty, giggly and full of laughter as the tale unfolds. If not, she immediately gives unmistakable signs of boredom or restlessness.

Our card games also belong to reminiscence therapy. Playing cards is an excellent way to conserve her ability in an activity she has always enjoyed and is very good at, not to mention the fact that it gives a huge boost to her self-esteem, especially when she wins.

Remembering positive memories makes Sylvia feel happy and confident, and noticeably more capable of doing routine everyday tasks. She is less clumsy, more content and more organised compared with how she is during her more challenging and confused periods. At these times she is able to manage tasks safely that at other times can cause her problems, such as making her own coffee, using the toilet or washing her hands. She even seems steadier on her feet.

In order to dip into positive memories, a carer can use more or less anything that is around the house or room of the person with dementia to help. It can be some memorabilia, a book, a photo album, a picture on the wall, an old magazine, or just a postcard. Anything that can be linked to a real event or person can be used.

As a therapy used in dementia care, reminiscence therefore has the double benefit of developing cognitive skills and supporting mental and emotional equilibrium, and, even more importantly, of enhancing quality of life. So when I am asked whether people can live a full and complete life after being diagnosed with dementia, a life that, from their perspective, is meaningful and unrestricted, my answer is a loud and definite 'Yes.'

CHAPTER
11

ALL MY RESPECT TO THE CACTUSES

Chronic forgetfulness often results in situations which bring a smile to the face, as when a mother sees her young child's first clumsy attempts at negotiating its way in an adult world. I cannot deny that I smile when I witness certain of Sylvia's actions, but I make sure it is an inner smile invisible to her and others as, understandably, she hates to be patronised or treated like a child.

In my view there appear to be two distinct types of action brought about by chronic forgetfulness. Both come from deep inside the person with dementia, and are maintained by a unique energy.

In the first group, I include all the ad hoc, sudden actions that arise spontaneously and last only for a short period of time – the strange 'off and on' sorts of action. These are reactions and responses to sudden stimuli that can be visual, emotional or physical; something that Sylvia experiences, and in that moment her mind connects it with an action, even if the association is sometimes very loose.

I have been searching for the car key for at least a quarter of an hour. I keep going round and round inside the house, lifting every cushion, book and paper, looking behind chairs and sofas, crawling on the carpet and looking under the furniture. Nothing! I know that I am the only one who uses the car. I last drove it yesterday afternoon and I usually leave the key on the hall table or on the shelf by the back door, but when I am exhausted, as I was yesterday, I sometimes find that I have put it down somewhere else.

Sylvia is ready to go out. I keep telling her that we are going to visit her favourite café by the river for a delicious slice of cake and a large hot chocolate. She is watching my unusual moves more and more suspiciously.

Every time I go past I explain that I am searching for the car key because we want to go to the café and it is too far to walk there.

'I wish I could help somehow,' she sighs.

Her impatience increases as the minutes pass, though she remains sitting on the little stool at the front door and is very sympathetic each time I remind her of the reason for the delay. Finally, I am at the point of giving up. Once more I explain to her what the situation is, admit that I cannot find the key and that without it we are stuck.

'Can I help?' she asks again.

Although I automatically rejected any offers of help from her at first as I did not believe that she could be of any assistance, I realise that if I get her involved, at least she will be kept busy and feel useful.

'Thank you. That's very kind of you. Could you start looking in the living room and I will look in the rest of the house?'

The fact that Sylvia now has an important mission changes her facial expression immediately. In contrast with her normal movements, she is suddenly quick-footed, maintains perfect balance without her walking stick and almost looks as if she is floating around her target room.

Sylvia's mood may have improved but the key is still lost.

However, every problem has a solution. I dial Linda's number. Luckily she is at home and has a spare key to Sylvia's car.

My lady and I set off on the short walk to Linda's house. She is very happy, as always, at the thought of going to see her daughter and chats away animatedly in the early spring sunshine.

As Sylvia pauses for breath I'm suddenly aware of an unusual sound accompanying us on our walk. Immediately I realise: I did not look for the key in the most obvious place!

The problem now is how can I approach Sylvia without offending her, causing her agitation and making her feel that I am blaming her?

I can definitely hear a faint jangling sound from the clothing under her coat, but I cannot search her in the street.

I sniff and remark that the cold spring air is making my nose run. I ask her if she has her handkerchief. She starts to look for her hanky and as usual, cannot find it, so I offer my help. Obediently she lets me open her coat and take a quick look in her cardigan and trouser pockets. The importance of having a hanky with us when we go out anywhere is something we both agree on.

When I reach the left trouser pocket, BINGO! – I can feel

the cold metal of the keyring.

'Oh, look what I've found!' I am pretending to be very surprised and trying to make out that this is an amazingly lucky coincidence. 'The car key! Who would have thought that it would be here?'

'It wasn't me,' Sylvia says immediately. 'Somebody must have put it there.'

As we are already more than halfway to Linda's house I decide to distract Sylvia with talk of her daughter and keep on walking. By the time we arrive, Sylvia cannot recall the upset concerning the key and enjoys the company of her daughter for a while.

We still manage to fit in our trip to the café.

Losing the car key was a one-off event and the lesson I learnt from it was never to put any important object anywhere that was accessible to Sylvia.

I must emphasise that people with dementia do not manipulate. Hiding the key in order to annoy or punish me would have demanded very complex and logical thinking that Sylvia and most people in an advanced stage of the condition are not able to achieve. What most likely happened is that Sylvia found the key while I was out of the room, picked it up and put it into her pocket with the intention of giving it to me when she saw me. She probably tried to find me and tell me that she had got it, but, by the time she found me, the original purpose and her recent actions had gone from her mind.

The second group of actions brought about by chronic forgetfulness includes the repetitive motions which recur daily at certain times of day, or in certain states of mind.

My personal favourite of Sylvia's compulsive actions is watering the plants every day after she has finished her after-lunch nap. Along with Sylvia's make-up routine, I find it fascinating that this action is indelibly stored in her mind as an essential part of her daily routine.

Sylvia gets up and finds the watering can, filling it with water. Her movements are very focused and accurate, her spirits soar, she knows she has a task to do. Her execution of the task is less competent though.

She goes into the living room. Precariously carrying the full can, she wanders around the table, staring at the vase with the artificial flowers in it, searching for real ones in the room.

As I do every single day, I go over to her and explain slowly and gently that the flowers in the vase are artificial, so they do not need water. As always, she looks very disappointed, and after a few seconds' hesitation, asks me where the flowers from the house have disappeared to.

'I know they were here. Somebody must have taken them and it is time to give them some water,' she insists. She is desperate.

I continue with the routine and walk her to the hall where she has five little pots of cactuses on the windowsill, shaking their non-existent heads and hands in fury at the prospect of being drowned again. However, any opposition is pointless; the water comes whether they need it or not.

All my respect to the cactuses for going through this daily torture, and yet still showing signs of being alive and taking kindly to being flooded day after day. Just when they have a chance to take a small breath as the last dose has evaporated and been absorbed from the pot, 'splash', here comes the next dousing.

I would never want to take this activity away from Sylvia as long as she can do it safely. I can see how important the watering routine is to her and respect the fact that it makes Sylvia's everyday life more complete. I believe that it is because she is allowed to carry on doing activities like this that she is able to retain a small part of her independence and as high a quality of life as possible.

■ ■ ■

Repetitive actions play a large part in Sylvia's night-time routine.

She says goodnight, but although it is ten o'clock, I know that her tired body will not be able to rest in her warm, soft bed for at least another hour.

I can hear her wandering around the house, repeatedly trying the front and back doors to check that they are locked properly, then checking that all the windows are closed and securely fastened too. I would prefer her to check several times that everything is secure rather than never, and while she is able to set her mind at rest for the night by going through this routine, will never discourage her from continuing to consider her personal safety.

The toilet is another essential part of her routine actions. I can hear the toilet flushing every ten minutes or so. Every time she passes the door, she sees the sign 'toilet' and remembers that she must go to the loo before she goes to bed. So in she goes, forgetting if she has been there before. Even if she cannot produce anything, she carefully flushes the toilet.

Sylvia also has an obsessive relationship with toilet paper as she uses it as a hanky to blow her nose. Every time she is on the loo, she filches a few extra sheets and stores them in her pockets. As a result, we have toilet paper all around the house. The main store is, naturally, in her room, but you can find bits of paper literally anywhere: tucked up her sleeves, in her bed, in her handbag and all kinds of other places.

My rule as a carer in this instance is simply threefold. Firstly, the habit is not dangerous for her or others, so I do nothing to stop it. Secondly, I have to make sure we have a sufficient supply. I have noticed Sylvia's anxiety level increasing when she sees that the current roll is running out and that she immediately becomes relaxed and content when she watches me restocking the toilets with supplies that are visible and accessible to her. My third task is to make sure that, strictly when Sylvia cannot see me doing it, I regularly collect the enormous amount of secretly hidden paper in order to keep the house as clean and tidy as possible and to reduce any excessive mess.

As well as toilet paper, a certain relish is a regular item on my shopping list. Although Sylvia insists on adding salt to her own food and constantly criticises me for making food that she claims is too hot and spicy even though I think it is completely tasteless, there is a particular brand of extremely hot horseradish that she always has to have on the side of her plate whatever is on the menu for our evening meal, whether it is pasta, chicken or fish.

I always add seasoning and spice to my food after serving up Sylvia's meal as there is no such thing as too hot for me; my Hungarian palate was brought up on lots of salt, pepper and hot paprika. Nevertheless, the one time I tasted the horseradish out of curiosity it is no exaggeration to say that the aftertaste and the 'flame' kept coming out through my nose, mouth and ears for a whole hour, even after my stomach, respiratory system and taste buds had finally returned to their normal functioning. It completely baffled me that someone who generally refuses any seasoning could happily eat this nightmare every day. I can only assume that Sylvia has a very pleasant and significant memory from her childhood connected to this horseradish. Perhaps her parents really liked it and it was always on the table at evening meals: happy times that she has carefully stored in her memory because they make her feel relaxed and at home.

I wonder at the cruel games the brain can play when I see Sylvia eating this sauce without the slightest grimace, yet if she notices a hint of pepper in her food, she pushes it away immediately as if it were the most disgusting thing in the world, saying it is too hot and there is no way she could ever eat it. However, on such occasions I try to validate her thoughts and feelings and I accept what she says and believes. Using this approach, I do not pay any more attention to the issue than it deserves and there is no need for further discussion or explanation on the matter.

However, one of Sylvia's compulsive habits that does require constant vigilance is her belief that she knows everybody.

With a father who was a playwright and a mother who was an actress, Sylvia's childhood was a constant social whirl. She was an only child and her parents took her with them wherever they went, so most of her younger years were spent in the bohemian, loud, smoky and very exciting world of mature people. Her adult life was also extremely sociable as she was a very active, intelligent, creative and entertaining personality, the kind of person who is always the life and soul of the party.

Sylvia therefore thinks that everyone is a friend or acquaintance.

At least once a day she opens the front door, steps outside smiling and says 'Hello' to literally everybody walking by. Luckily she is very well known in the area so quite a few people stop for a minute and have a few words with her. Others say 'Hello' back, some just wave and keep on walking and there are those who ignore her and walk past her as if she is not there.

This habit could be very dangerous and unsafe if Sylvia were living alone, as she has been known to invite strangers into the house, believing that she knows them well. Mostly people are good-hearted and kind, but it could easily be otherwise.

I have to choose my reaction and words very carefully when Sylvia is excessively friendly to strangers as reality confrontation is never the answer in dementia. I cannot say to her that she is putting herself in danger and that none of these people has ever been a friend of hers. She firmly believes the opposite and in her inner world she actually knows them.

My response is therefore once again based on reassurance and distraction. I never treat her like a child or patronise her, but I must always have something better to offer that leads her away from the door. What this 'other thing' is can be different for every person with dementia because it has to be something that works well and is tempting to that individual. With Sylvia, it can be an outing, going for a drive together, an interesting programme on TV, a task that I ask her to help with or one of her favourites: a chocolate.

The firm belief that she does know everyone makes me smile to myself whenever I watch Sylvia reading the paper. She makes comments on every single photo she sees as she thinks she knows the people in the pictures.

'Look, here is Ann, oh, my dear friend's daughter. What a lovely picture of her!'

She turns the page and spots the next photo.

'Julia, Julia, my dearest, how nice to see you again.' She smiles happily.

Of course, she has absolutely no connection whatsoever with the faces in the photos, but the behaviour is harmless so I let her satisfy her need to have company and friends, even if they are imaginary ones in this case. After all, it gives her a positive emotional boost that fundamentally supports her mental equilibrium.

The only time I do have to act is when a memory evoked by a stranger's photo in the paper is too upsetting or has a negative impact on Sylvia's well-being. I will never forget Sylvia's extreme reaction the day when Margaret Thatcher died.

The death of the former prime minister was broadcast as 'breaking news' on most of the TV channels and Sylvia's behaviour was very peculiar as soon as she heard the news. She kept repeating that she could not believe that her best friend had gone at so young an age, although Mrs Thatcher was actually 87 years old when she died.

I observe Sylvia warily and carefully, for, who knows, she might really have known Margaret Thatcher. Whether she did or not, I do not want to cause her unnecessary trauma by questioning what she says or how she feels. I cannot check the facts with Linda and Kevin as they are away on holiday.

One of the biggest difficulties of the day is the problem

of distraction. Normally I am quite good at this, but I keep running into obstacles as it is extremely difficult to find a TV or radio channel where they are talking about anything else.

The problem remains over the next few days as the news continues to be the cover story in most papers, underlining the importance of the event. It seems as though the whole world is shouting the news into Sylvia's face wherever we turn.

In moments like this, there is only one way for the carer to react to the severe distress of the person with dementia, and that is to listen, understand and reassure. I nod and sympathise every time the subject of Mrs Thatcher's death comes up, astonished by Sylvia's detailed stories of their friendship.

In Sylvia's mind it is an incontrovertible fact that she first met Margaret Thatcher in Derby when the Iron Lady visited the design company she worked for. They then become very close friends and had been closely in touch ever since. They had last met only just a week before, when they had had a cup of tea together.

Such sudden and intense emotional reactions triggered by news which does not have any connection with the person with dementia are most likely based on a similar feeling towards someone the person actually knew and has lost. In this way, grief is transferred.

Sylvia's overreaction seemed to be caused by the confusion that overwhelmed her like rivers of lava when she kept hearing about the death of Mrs Thatcher which caused her to experience an intense feeling of grief. Unable to match this feeling with the real faces of the real people from her own life, as her mind can no longer remember them, she connected it to the most obvious choice, the familiar and famous face of an important figure. The instant reaction of the mind of a person with dementia is to create false memories to support the emotional need. These memories then disturbed Sylvia further, and so acutely that only tears could bring some relief, tears which I believe stood for all the people Sylvia is no longer able to recall or grieve for who have passed away; all those family members and friends who once were very close to her, but are now gone.

Sylvia only got her equilibrium back when the news disappeared from the headlines a few days later. By the time everything went back to what was normal for her and she could return to her familiar routines, I was utterly exhausted as the constant reassurance had taken its toll on my energy levels. When Sylvia was finally settled and fast asleep having enjoyed an uninterrupted evening of her favourite quiz show and detective stories, I sighed out loud with relief. 'At last it's quiet. Thank goodness for that!'

However, an unanswered question kept gnawing away at the back of my mind. As soon as Linda was back from her trip I asked if it was possible that her mother could have been friends with the first female prime minister of the UK. I must admit I was relieved to learn that my original feeling was confirmed: they had never met.

■ ■ ■

CHAPTER

12

THE SECRET LANGUAGE

In the Western world the condition of dementia is fortunately taken seriously. A dementia-friendly infrastructure has been built up over time and this is constantly being developed and expanded according to changing needs within society. Based on years of experience and research, experiments and creative ideas, carers can choose from dozens of different options for ways to help people with dementia live a complete and satisfying life. Drawing on these techniques and the various services available, carers in day centres, respite homes and care homes, and those working in in-house care can all provide specifically tailored, very individual methods of care for people with this condition.

In dementia care the phrase 'the silent carer' refers to the environment, which is at least as important as the personal relationship between the person with dementia and the carer in creating a supportive, high quality of life. A well-planned and well-set-up therapeutic environment is vital as a framework for those living with this mental condition.

The Dementia Design Audit Tool has been developed by the Dementia Services Development Centre at the University of Stirling in Scotland as a result of focus groups of people with dementia and their family members suggesting what aspects of design are important for them. Key design principles, such as safety and security, keeping things small-scale, familiarity, provision for planned wandering, visual access, stimulation and privacy are always kept in mind when ensuring that a person is living in a dementia-friendly environment. However, findings from the focus groups indicated that certain elements of design are less important than others. A friendly welcome received from carers or family members, a pleasant smell experienced on their return to the place where they are living, being served attractive-looking food and having outside spaces they can use were all rated as more important than en-suite facilities by people with this disease.

It is worth bearing in mind how vital greetings and initial impressions are when coming into contact with a person with dementia for the first time. Taking the time to ensure that a person is made to feel welcome is the foundation of a good relationship whereas the opposite causes estrangement.

I found the fact that most people with dementia scored having en-suite facilities as 'not important' surprised me at first. However, I then realised that this does not mean that they would not use them. People with dementia focus more on the function of a bathroom, rather than on its proximity, design or appearance, whereas when it comes to food, for example, visual pleasure is vital – food needs to look appealing and appetising. The nutritional value of food is of course important, but the quality of the presentation makes all the difference. A small aesthetic touch and a little creativity can achieve a miracle and encourage a person with the condition to eat and enjoy their meal.

The importance of things being visually appealing must be taken into account in all aspects of dementia care. Keeping a tidy appearance and maintaining a high level of personal hygiene is a basic requirement when working as a carer, but I made an interesting discovery about one lady with dementia who I was looking after that took this requirement to a new level.

This elderly lady was very challenging and quite often abusive, with a history of verbal and physical aggression. She was bedridden, so her life was confined to a single room. In the first few weeks when we were getting to know each other, I observed everything she said or did. Of course there were things over which I had no control, but there were times when there were no obvious causes for the significant differences in her behaviour between one day and another.

When I had time to think about what else I had done differently on the days when she had been more agitated and verbally abusive, I suddenly realised. I had dressed differently. I recalled 'good' days when I had put on something nicer than my usual casual, comfortable outfits. 'It's worth giving it a go!' I thought.

So I tried dressing the way I would normally dress for a special occasion, like wearing a smart white blouse or an attractive scarf, and she was definitely more cooperative. She never missed a chance to say a few words about my outfit and would initiate a conversation about the pattern of my dress or ask me to stand on a chair so that she could see what I was wearing on my feet. What I did was really only common sense. It was simply a small adjustment on my part in order to accommodate an individual's unique taste and expectations, but it made a huge difference to the attitude of the person I was caring for.

The importance of maintaining a positive, healthy balance in personality and self-concept of a person with this disease, while also supporting their interaction with the real world, has already been emphasised – the 'I am still here' approach is fundamental in guiding people with dementia so that they can enjoy a life full of cheer, fun and joyful moments in which they feel useful and occupied. 'Guiding' is the watchword for carers working in dementia care.

Day centres meet the needs of people with dementia at the same time as helping their carers to be able to carry on with their own lives, routines and jobs as far as is possible during the day. Respite homes give carers a longer break. In both facilities people with dementia are safe, the environment has been designed to be dementia-friendly, the staff are specially trained and the activities tailor-made. People gain a great deal of satisfaction from spending time and working together with others with the same mental condition, doing activities designed to meet the challenging needs of the group.

Before I came to the UK I was responsible for a respite home in Australia that was part of a federal government-funded programme providing short-term accommodation for people living with dementia. These people usually lived at home and had family or friends supporting them, but would come to the respite home during times when their carers needed a few days' break, or had something very important to do that took them away from the caring role, such as hospital treatment, business trips or other family members' visits.

The safety and comfort levels, the clearly recognisable labels and signs, the colours, textures and contrasts in shape and size, the furniture, the ornaments and, last but not least, the staff in the respite home all contributed to the dementia-friendly environment, and I was lucky enough to have the chance to continue to develop the facility in consultation with the staff.

It was decided to adopt an idea I had come across at a conference and small solar-powered lights were installed along the pathways around the home. After dark, the lights lit up the route so that those staying at the respite home who, very typically of people with dementia, were prone to wander, could satisfy their need safely and enjoyably instead of being shut unwillingly inside the home. They wandered, but it was a guided wandering, adhering to a circuit, so offering an infinite opportunity for that particular activity. The electric gate that enclosed the property could only be worked by staff at the home with a remote control, but there were never any reports of would-be escapees. In this way, the definition of what would be considered as 'normal' was extended, while staying within the bounds of what was safe for the individual. The gate was more of a visual than a physical boundary as none of the residents ever thought of leaving the centre because they were content doing whatever they wanted to while they were there.

In the daytime, the respite home garden provided plenty of activities for those who liked to spend time outdoors. The garden had been planned so that it was dementia-friendly, with plants, flowers, statues and fountains carefully chosen to stimulate all the senses. An interesting rock feature was created and benches were positioned all round the garden as most of the people who came to stay were elderly and liked to have somewhere to sit and rest. It was a real pleasure to witness their joy as they talked about certain flowers, and how the shapes and colours of the animal statues made them smile.

One of the people with dementia who came to stay regularly was Charlie and he is someone I will never forget. Before his first visit I met his family and learnt that Charlie had had a huge garden of his own and had spent most of his free time gardening. When I drew up a care plan in agreement with Charlie and his family, the garden featured heavily.

Charlie loves having responsibility for watering the plants in the summer. Someone always keeps an eye on him to make sure he does not overdo it as he is 82 years old. He never misses out on a single plant, tub, planter, pot or window box, and the rock feature and the statues all get a wash too.

Old habits die hard and when he finishes, he knows that the job is not complete until the hose is stored away properly. When the member of staff with him shows him each time how the hose automatically rewinds into its reel he beams with amazement and delight.

He is always soaking wet by the time he completes his job and makes his entrance into the living room, announcing 'I've finished' to everybody who has been watching him through the windows. There is an ethereal happiness on his face. While a carer changes him into dry clothes in his room he is still talking about the joy he has just experienced.

At the back of the respite home there was a relatively large barbecue and picnic area. I believe the change in scenery arising from having a meal outdoors in the sun and the fresh air has a good effect on the bond that links care-givers to care-takers. Furthermore, the sun's rays work as a natural battery charger, reinvigorating every individual and making them more active and lively, and bringing a smile to the face of even the most introverted person with dementia. By the end of a day spent outdoors, children have used up all their excess energy and go to bed with an agreeable tiredness, calm and relaxed, full of lovely memories and 'buzz'. This is exactly how it works with people with dementia too.

Humans are intrinsically social beings, whether they are living with a mental condition or not. Of course, overcrowded spaces have a contrary effect, but being part of a small community has an outstandingly positive influence on the well-being of those living with dementia. This is especially true if people with the same or similar disease can be brought together. Then the mutual impact they have on each other is instantly detectable.

I can barely describe what I felt when I witnessed two ladies finding a way to communicate with each other, without any assistance, during the short period they spent together in the respite home.

One of the Marias – they are both called Maria – is a charming, very neat old lady of Spanish origin. Due to her dementia, she can no longer speak English and only understands a sprinkling of basic English words. Even fluent Spanish speakers find her Spanish difficult to understand. This lovely Maria spends most of her time in the company of another Maria, who speaks a mixture of strongly accented English and Croatian, which was her mother tongue.

These two unbelievably adorable Marias sit side by side on the sofa for hours, gesticulating wildly or holding hands, looking at magazines together, but constantly talking to each other, giggling and laughing a great deal. They certainly speak a secret language that only they understand and which only works between the two of them. It is a pure delight to see.

At the same time as guiding people with dementia so that they can enjoy as full a life as possible, carers must be aware of and monitor any signs of discomfort or pain.

It is quite common for those living with this mental condition to deny pain. It is not because they want to hide it, but rather that they are frequently unable to recognise the physical symptoms. Even when they do recognise the pain, they often cannot put this feeling into words.

In hospitals it is frequent practice to ask patients to describe their pain level on a scale of 1 to 10. This information can only come from that particular person as he or she is the one experiencing it; the level of pain stays invisible to everyone else. However, when it comes to dementia, this sort of self-assessment is impossible as the cognitive impairment of people with the disease simply does not allow them to answer this question correctly. The resulting dangers of this issue are obvious. For example, experiencing pain when peeing is the main indication for urinary tract infections.

The Abbey Pain Scale[10] – a pain scale measuring tool developed specifically to measure pain levels in people with dementia – provides the effective solution to this problem. By using this special chart it is possible to get a relatively exact picture, and to quantify the current pain level of someone with dementia.

On the chart there are six different aspects for the carer to observe: vocalisation, facial expression, change in body language, behavioural change such as increased confusion, physiological change like temperature, pulse or blood pressure, and physical changes such as skin tears or pressure areas. For each aspect there are four possible answers followed by a score to circle: absent 0, mild 1, moderate 2 or severe 3. Following observation and filling in the chart, the carer arrives at a 'total pain score', which can then be matched to the approximate level of pain and the carer also records the type of pain (chronic, acute, or acute on chronic).

The Cornell Scale for Depression in Dementia (CSDD)[11] works on a similar principle and enables the carer to estimate an individual's level of depression if depression is thought to be an issue.

When dealing with dementia, it is very helpful to have different tools which make care work easier and more accurate in a world of forever 'I don't know' and 'I'm not sure', but my considered view is that observation is the real key, with or without any charts or forms. Common sense is one of the most underestimated tools in a carer's armoury. The only thing that is absolutely necessary when looking after someone living with dementia is a base line; everything else, such as behavioural changes, appetite, level of confusion, agitation and so on, can then be compared to that.

Awareness and understanding of ageing and dementia are increasing as a result of various initiatives in a number of different countries. As a means of enhancing social interaction initiatives for people from diverse cultural background the CALD (Culturally and Linguistically Diverse) Intergenerational Dementia Project[12] in Australia was a breakthrough.

The project organised links between three primary schools, three secondary schools and three mixed-national Migrant Resource Centres (MRCs) to foster the sharing and continuation of traditions between generations of the Macedonian, Italian and Vietnamese communities. Schoolchildren shared a morning of weaving lessons, cooking and dancing with people with dementia from the MRCs in Planned Activity Groups (PAGs). These successful events were then followed by the people with dementia visiting the schools and participating in activities there.

The original project and the continuing initiatives of this kind fulfil two very important functions apart from the continuing of traditions: firstly, they set up an environment that brings out the caring impulses and the willingness to teach in people who have this disease, giving them the sense of being needed and useful. Having an audience of schoolchildren carefully watching and listening intently to everything they do or say, creates feelings of self-worth and self-confidence as they are given the important role of educating the younger generation. Secondly, it helps to eradicate from young minds the stigma which accompanies this mental condition by giving schoolchildren a very sophisticated and real picture of what the term 'dementia' means in practice.

In the UK, Dementia awareness and intergenerational exchange in schools, a pioneer project supporting dementia-friendly communities, was set up in order to improve awareness and understanding of dementia among primary and secondary schoolchildren, and the Alzheimer's Society's Youth Engagement Project is taking their initiative forward.

The young people taking part in these projects develop relationships with people with dementia, find out about their life experiences and get to know the people underneath the condition. They learn about the disease and the ways in which people with dementia can be supported. They learn to approach people who have dementia in a more effective way, treating them naturally and continuing to see them as valuable members of society, with the same basic need to be loved and well treated as every other individual. The knowledge the children gain is then often passed on to other family members.

Another inspirational initiative, ARTZ (Artists for Alzheimer's) was started in America and is based on the positive effects of art. This programme organises a huge variety of activities, such as museum and exhibition tours, circus and concert visits, dance, art and music workshops, for people with dementia and their carers within their own community. The stimulus provided by these events boosts the emotional activity of people with this condition as well as their mental well-being, and there is good evidence that they reduce the four As in Alzheimer's: anxiety, agitation, aggression and apathy.

In a 'debriefing session' after every event each carer asks the person they are supporting to recall any particular highlights if they can. These are noted down, together with any successful or less successful moments observed by the carers, in order to build up a picture of the effect of the programme on each individual and of their particular likes and dislikes.

This feedback establishes a good baseline for each individual's person-centred care plan.

Although people with dementia often cannot recall the event itself later, they will still remember certain melodies, lyrics, words or pictures that they heard or saw when they are reminded of them; the positive association these things have is emotional rather than logical or verbal.

∎ ∎ ∎

Sylvia has not used either day care or respite care facilities since I have been looking after her, but we do take advantage of any dementia-friendly cultural events in the local area, as well as attending concerts for the general public. Even though these activities can turn her biological clock upside down because of the late hour she finally gets into bed, there is no doubt that they have a beneficial effect.

It is wonderful to watch Sylvia singing along, clapping and smiling and very helpful for me to be able to note down how she reacts to every single melody we hear.

In order to be able to focus on her own joy arising from a concert, Sylvia must have absolutely no doubt in her mind that I know exactly what to do in any situation and that she is in safe hands. I always book seats near an exit and at the end of a row. I try to avoid crowds by carefully timing our arrival at the concert hall, we wait in our seats at the end until most of the audience has left, and I protect and help her on any stairs. If I see a trigger coming that could cause her to feel anxious or agitated, I keep offering reassurance: 'Don't worry about others coming and going; just focus on your steps, Sylvia, only one at the time.' I constantly reassure her, making it clear that I am there for her; everything is under control and nothing bad can happen to her.

For me, these occasions are not about the entertainment or the enjoyment, even if the event is excellent, as I am continually keeping an eye on Sylvia in case she needs anything. If I see that she has a runny nose, I give her a hanky to save her the trouble of looking for it in the dark. If I notice she is becoming restless in her seat, I ask if she needs to go to the toilet. All the time I am carrying out a sort of mindreading based on very close and constant observation. I always try to be one step ahead of any problem which might occur.

On our return home, Sylvia's face fills with life, her eyes sparkle and her tiredness or weakness melt away as we sing one of the songs she has enjoyed together. Her night-time routine is completed in double-quick time as she is focused, cooperative and happy. When I finally say goodnight to her there is a smile on her face as she shuts her eyes and I can see that she is going to remain calm all night, with no wandering or confusion.

I do not need any encouragement to fall asleep either, but for different reasons. After an outing like this, when I have had to be Sylvia's physical and emotional rock, I feel completely drained, but Sylvia's happy, smiling face is the last picture in my mind as I shut my eyes.

CHAPTER
13

'I'VE GOT BLOODY DEMENTIA!'

Sylvia and I are watching a film together and there is a scene in which the main character invites her friends to visit her grandmother with dementia. The conversation they all have at a table in the care home garden makes the grandmother's dementia painfully clear and then two carers in uniform are suddenly shown in the background running after a hysterical, screaming resident, trying to catch him so that they can put a straitjacket on him. The main character turns towards her friends and says: 'I would never do their job, even if they paid me a fortune.'

I scan Sylvia's face discreetly, to see whether she understands what is happening and whether she is drawing any comparison between the scene in the film and her real life, but there is no flicker of comprehension. It appears that she is listening to the dialogue, but she cannot see any connection between two different scenes in the film, and definitely not between the film scenario and her own situation.

Sometimes it happens that for a fleeting moment Sylvia is aware of her condition, just like when the sun comes out briefly before the wind whisks the clouds back over its face and it is gone, its place in the sky usurped yet again by the clouds.

The fact that she has dementia has never been kept a secret from Sylvia. 'Dementia' is a word she has come across many times and in many situations. I know that when Sylvia's live-in carer service was set up, the regional manager responsible for her care paid her a home visit and, as part of the initial assessment, Sylvia was involved in creating her own care plan. It is not possible to avoid mentioning dementia when creating as accurate as possible a baseline from which the carer would begin his or her work and Sylvia's whole family has always talked openly about her condition.

According to the Alzheimer's Society, it is important to investigate denial or acceptance of the dementia diagnosis by close family members. For example, if, in the face of a formal medical opinion, a relative keeps insisting that their beloved relative is now much better, or that there is nothing unusual about their behaviour, or that there are no changes in their daily routines or habits, this person is denying reality.

It is crucial that denial is confronted, because this dissonance between perception and reality can have a detrimental effect on the individual's own physical and mental health and also can leave the person with dementia without sufficient help and support, increasing his or her confusion and distress.

Accepting the diagnosis of dementia is not an easy process, either for the individual affected, or for their family, but it is the only way of ensuring that any future difficulties can be properly dealt with. Once people acknowledge their feelings about dementia, they take a huge step forward towards acceptance. Tears must fall and feelings of devastation, anger or fear must be embraced, because without allowing real feelings to surface, no progress can be made.

It is impossible to say whether one or a combination of occasions has caused the 'verdict' of dementia to be etched into Sylvia's brain, but a particular incident made it starkly obvious to me and to Linda that she is constantly living with that knowledge.

When Linda or I take Sylvia out to a public place, people often kindly offer their help. The sight of a very fragile and vulnerable-looking old lady leaning heavily on the arm of her companion frequently prompts strangers to ask, 'Do you need a hand?' or 'Are you all right?' Linda, Sylvia and I always appreciate and express our gratitude for their thoughtfulness, and say a warm 'Thank you, we are fine' and are often glad to accept their practical assistance. Then, one day when Linda took her mother on an outing into town to give me a break, a similar suggestion from a kind stranger was met with an entirely unexpected response from her mother.

'I've got bloody dementia!' Sylvia screamed at him.

There was no apparent trigger for such an extreme reaction. Luckily, by the time she got home, Sylvia had forgotten what had happened. Nothing like this has ever happened again, although Sylvia has experienced similar kindness and solicitude from countless strangers since. However, neither Linda nor I, once Linda had told me what had happened, has ever been able to erase the incident from our memories. We were both completely taken aback by Sylvia's totally out of character and startlingly aggressive response to a stranger. However, perhaps on this one occasion it was Sylvia's *alter ego*, the person with dementia, rather than the fragile old lady who got fed up with being patronised and treated differently by another human being.

The fact that someone is told he or she has dementia and has to live with that fact can create a multitude of different feelings in the person given this diagnosis. The whole gamut of emotions is experienced: frustration, anger, sadness and depression. Negative feelings triggered by the disease, together with unhelpful reactions from others, can explain to a certain extent why many people accept very limited help and support, or none at all, after receiving their diagnosis. Further contributory factors to this rejection of help could be that many people with dementia become convinced that they are stupid and believe that having a mental condition such as dementia is shameful.

During those brief moments when people with dementia can see things really clearly, even in an advanced stage of the condition, they realise that nothing will ever again be the same as it was before their diagnosis and this is naturally very difficult to accept. Constantly experiencing clumsiness while carrying out very simple routines, such as taking off an item of clothing, making breakfast, or having a shower, can be devastating. Just as devastating for people with dementia is when they are still physically capable of doing all of these things, have good hearing, sight, mobility and have retained their sense of touch, but they do not know what to do with the mug they are holding, they have no idea where the coffee is or what they are doing in the kitchen anyway. What did they come into the room for?

The role of a carer is to encourage people with dementia to complete as many tasks as they can independently as long as they can be done safely, and to try to help restore these very simple routines by giving a little 'push' or guidance when needed.

I often find Sylvia's necklace in the freezer, a milk bottle in the kitchen cupboard, and the sliced bread under the kitchen sink among the cleaning products. It can happen in a matter of a few minutes, when I go to the toilet, for instance. Then the searching and replacing starts, and I play a guessing game of where might she have put this or that.

This particular behaviour is most likely caused by the lack of ability to orientate in time or place, but sometimes such a compulsive action can be a sign of boredom, of feeling unsafe or anxious, or the result of an irrational idea.

If the mistakes come to light, people with dementia realise once more that there are certain things they cannot do correctly or the way they used to. That is why it is unhelpful to draw attention to these mistakes, especially because any intention is well meant; there is no wish to deceive. The best way to deal with them is just to ignore what has happened and, like an invisible helping angel, simply and quietly put everything back where it belongs.

When Sylvia makes a mistake in my presence and somehow becomes aware of it, she finds it traumatic. On these occasions she often verbalises her sadness and the fact she feels like 'a useless idiot', 'a stupid woman', and I truly feel sorry for her. Sometimes she cries, and moments like this are very often accompanied by lethargy and depression. At other times when similar things happen, she cannot verbalise exactly what is wrong, but realises that something is not quite right. She can only express her feelings by comments such as: 'I don't know what has happened, but everything looks different', 'I feel I should be doing something else' or 'I have no idea what I should be doing'.

In my care work I have found it tremendously helpful to think that diseases have their own 'vaccines', so when challenging behaviour occurs, there are always techniques that can be used in response to it and these techniques can also be used in prevention as well. Practising positive communication is something I make a conscious effort to do when I am with Sylvia. It is built on a helpful, kind and friendly – but not too friendly – attitude that helps me get her actively engaged in completing different tasks so that she feels some sense of achievement, and her self-esteem is boosted, as is her sense of having a degree of independence.

The curse of dementia can also be its blessing as one of the main characteristics of the condition, forgetting, is the reason why distraction techniques work so very effectively. An exaggeratedly positive reaction, that would be a little excessive when dealing with a healthy-minded adult, works well with Sylvia, especially if I want to make her forget an unpleasant or negative experience. For example, when I show joy and surprise exclaiming: 'Look at that lovely cat in the garden!' the cat is there. I am not lying. I have just scanned our surroundings in order to find something that would offer a good opportunity to distract Sylvia's mind away from something that is bothering her. The effort of thinking about and processing this new information means that Sylvia is now focused on something thoroughly positive, which engenders pleasant feelings, and the disturbing thoughts disappear.

Simple mundane household tasks, such as peeling potatoes, can help to restore the mental balance of people with dementia, making them feel wanted and useful. The very fact of being able to do something that is actually helpful eases their troubled minds and can give satisfaction for hours. I make every effort to involve Sylvia in easy household tasks, especially those that I know she likes doing, but only when the task is very straightforward and she is physically capable of performing it.

However, do not be misled into thinking that this assistance will make the carer's responsibilities or work any easier. On the contrary, when Sylvia helps, everything always takes twice as long as doing the task on my own.

I need to distract Sylvia. Having taken a biscuit from the tin, she has just put the open tin of biscuits in the washing-up bowl full of water rather than replace the lid and put it back in the cupboard. She is berating herself and close to tears.

I immediately steer her away from the sink and suggest that we make her favourite cottage pie recipe together for lunch, asking her if she would like to help by peeling the potatoes. She readily agrees and I sit her down at the table facing away from the evidence of her mistake. I put on her apron and get everything she needs ready.

Once I have successfully engaged Sylvia in her task, I quickly throw away the sodden biscuits and dry up the tin before I start to cook the mince. However, it is difficult to focus on my own job as I have to keep a close watch on what she is doing, constantly checking whether she is coping or whether she needs some help.

The potato peel is going everywhere: on the floor, on the chairs, in Sylvia's hair, on her shoes, and her apron is covered in peelings. After peeling each potato she asks: 'Now tell me, where should I put this?' even though I have put a bowl ready and waiting right in front of her.

Nonetheless, it is worth it. As I get on with chopping the onions I am pleased to see that Sylvia is in a good mood. She is smiling a lot and becoming very talkative, even witty at times. I remind myself that dementia care is not about rushing, but is the complete opposite. The only way to achieve success is through spending time and being patient.

I have to surreptitiously check and finish off peeling all the potatoes before cooking them, but Sylvia has enjoyed herself. By working together to create our meal there is no doubt that Sylvia's quality of life has been improved and that she no longer feels an idiot or different from anyone else.

The road along which the carer of someone with dementia travels is paved with a constant mixture of stress, tiredness, frustration and sadness, as well as a disconcerting tendency to apathy at times. By getting to know as much as possible about the particular type of dementia the people being cared for are living with and by researching locally available communities and support groups, together with specific national organisations and foundations set up for the purpose of supporting and informing about this particular condition, carers can do a great deal to help themselves.

For those facing the diagnosis of dementia, particularly in its most common form, the Alzheimer's Society is a good starting point for getting to know about the different phases and the expected progression of the disease. Fortunately, this information is widely available nowadays, and can be accessed in a variety of ways: in books, online or from local Alzheimer's Society offices. There are also Freephone helplines available where various different professionals offer help and advice.

In the case of a specific diagnosis of Alzheimer's disease, the most common system for evaluating deterioration, developed by Dr Barry Reisberg of New York University,[13] breaks the progression of Alzheimer's disease into seven stages, while emphasising that, since Alzheimer's affects people in different ways, each person will experience symptoms or progress through the stages of Alzheimer's quite differently.

In Stage 1, there is practically no memory loss yet detectable and there are hardly any visible or outwardly measurable signs of abnormal brain function. Diagnosis is based solely on the result of brain scans and other advanced and sophisticated diagnostic tools which are the only way to pick up the specific changes in the brain which begin years before any outward signs of the disease appear.

In Stage 2, a very mild decline is detectable, although this can be confused with the general decline of ageing and is therefore still very hard to pick up. The individual will still do well on memory tests and the disease is unlikely to be detected by physicians or family members.

By Stage 3, relatives or close friends may begin to notice memory and cognitive problems. Performance in memory and cognitive tests is affected and physicians will be able to detect impaired cognitive function.

In this stage, observers may notice that the affected person has difficulties in finding the right words during conversation, has a problem planning and organising ideas, or remembering names of recent acquaintances.

Stage 4 is the first stage where the signs of Alzheimer's are more obvious to a close observer. The chronic forgetfulness can now be seen causing failure in ability to recall current events, difficulty with holding conversations, and with basic maths and counting. The person affected is now losing the ability to perform complex tasks such as dealing with finances and paying bills. Inexplicable mood changes are also likely to occur, especially in mentally challenging situations.

Stage 5 is characterised by moderate to severe cognitive decline. The gaps in memory are getting wider and more obvious. The individual will now need help in performing certain tasks, including basic, everyday routines such as brushing teeth or making coffee.

In this stage, there are definite signs of confusion relating to spatial orientation, time and date. People affected can have difficulty in remembering their own address or phone number as well as problems recalling important dates in their life, such as their birthday, the year they left school or the day they got married.

Also typical is a lack of judgement in simple issues such as what they should wear today, as it requires a relatively complex level of thinking to acknowledge the season and the weather first, and then to make a sensible decision about what clothing is appropriate. On the other hand, people in Stage 5 retain a measure of functionality. Typically they can still bathe and go to the toilet independently. They also usually still know their family members and some details of their personal histories, especially their childhood and youth.

In Stage 6, cognitive decline is fast and severe. This is the stage when constant supervision and professional care are needed, when confusion or lack of awareness of environment and surroundings occur, and when major personality changes can take place.

People in Stage 6 do not remember things which happened only moments ago, like Sylvia who can make five or six cups of tea for herself between 3 and 4 o'clock every afternoon. I do not want to upset her by making her aware of her forgetfulness and the fact that she has done something wrong. Each time Sylvia gets out a clean cup and puts the kettle on once more, I remind myself that the point of the activity is making the tea, not necessarily drinking it. It does not matter if five out of six cups of tea end up by being poured down the kitchen sink, but it does make me realise that, three and a half years on from my arrival as Sylvia's carer, the disease has progressed considerably.

Behavioural problems can occur where there is insufficient assistance with activities of daily living such as toileting and bathing. This is the stage when assistance with dressing and appearance are required, when different types of fastenings, such as zips, buttons and hooks and eyes, require superhuman efforts on the part of the person with Alzheimer's. Written reminders will now be needed: how to use the toilet paper, or flush the loo. There will also be physical signs indicating that the dementia has moved into a more severe stage. Partial or full incontinence may occur on a daily basis, showing the loss in connection between the brain and muscle control of bowel and bladder. It is not unusual for repetitive words or actions to become evident, and this is the stage when aimless wandering may start, with the resulting increased risk of having a fall or getting lost.

In Stage 6, people with Alzheimer's are more suspicious and may keep blaming others for any mistake they make. Due to their condition, they may report stolen jewellery or money that they believe someone has taken. Although most of these cases turn out to be false allegations, it does no harm to be aware of this possibility and to take care to be above suspicion in case it happens. I know from experience that it is not at all easy to distract people with Alzheimer's from negative thoughts when they are in this severe stage. Nor is it easy just to be on hand day and night, as there is always something unexpected happening. I realise that I have been saying: 'This is the first time Sylvia has done this' or 'I've never known her do that before' to Linda a lot recently. I now recognise that the best I can do is to exercise my common sense, to use all the information I have at my disposal and to be prepared for the most surprising behaviours.

Also noticeable may be an inability to recognise faces except those of close friends and relatives, and an inability to remember most details of personal history. In Stage 6, people with Alzheimer's have difficulties in recalling names, even those of people living with them whom they see every day. Sylvia often calls me 'sweetie' or 'dear' for the simple reason that she has forgotten my real name. A similar example is when I looked after someone living with dementia with Lewy bodies, whose habit was to give names that she could remember to everybody around her. For her, I was 'Patricia'.

In Stage 7, the final stage of Alzheimer's, people experience a very severe decline. They lose the ability to respond to their environment or to communicate. While they may still be able to utter some words and phrases, they have no insight into their condition and need full assistance with all activities of daily living. Reaching the stage of end-of-life palliative care, they might lose their ability to swallow, their appetite, or both. Involuntary reflexes can take over control of the body, and frequent choking and coughing can occur when they try to take a sip of their drink. In this stage, the carer's job is to maintain hygiene and dignity by providing a high standard of physical comfort, and by observing people with Alzheimer's even more closely as it is likely that they will have lost all ability to verbalise anything. By reading their faces and by piecing together all the different puzzles presented by their behaviour by means of some guesswork, a carer can work out what is bothering them and what feels good.

Care involves several forms of interaction other than communication with words and non-verbal communication, such as touch, look, taste, hearing or smell for example, plays a much greater role during palliative care. It can give people with Alzheimer's a feeling of peace and contentment to listen to their favourite music, or to hear someone reading from their favourite novel or their favourite poem. Feeling a soft touch on their skin and smelling their familiar, long-accustomed lotion on their body, or looking at lovely fresh flowers in the room, or, in my personal experience, holding a rosary, are all ways to create a pleasant, relaxed feeling. Just because people have reached the final stage in their life, a carer must not forget about their rich personal history. The fact is they are still the same people with all their individual likes and dislikes that, ideally, by this stage, a carer will have got to know very well. Carers must base their use of different methods and equipment to make people with Alzheimer's as comfortable as possible in Stage 7 based on this cumulative knowledge.

Maintaining a high standard of personal hygiene is particularly important in this stage: refreshing strip washes, regularly changed pads, bedsheet and nightwear, and providing frequent mouth care. Brushing hair may seem a minor thing. Most people hardly notice it as part of a basic morning routine. However, if people are unable to do it on their own, it is very soothing to have someone do it for them.

There is one final and seemingly unimportant ingredient in the care of people with Alzheimer's in Stage 7: fresh air. When people with Alzheimer's are confined to their room or to their bed, if there is no contraindication in their physical condition, open the window for five minutes a few times a day and let the oxygen-rich fresh air fill the room.

■ ■ ■

There is no definite dividing line between each of the seven different stages of Alzheimer's. Overlaps occur because individuals with a unique character and brain structure, and with their own personal lifestyle are involved. Some people will experience certain symptoms later, some of them earlier, than the classification would indicate. Nevertheless, knowing the stages clarifies just what significant behavioural changes and necessary lifestyle modifications the affected person and their family are facing.

The journey of a person with Alzheimer's holds unforeseeable difficulties for the future for everybody involved, so it is no wonder that a wide range of emotional reactions takes place on the way. It is totally understandable for people to be sad, angry or depressed at times, especially for those who are having one of those lucid moments when reality breaks through their mind's confusion for a second and they become aware, briefly, of what dementia has changed in their life and in their personality.

Making decisions about the best possible care for the final stage is tough. Whether to choose in-home care or care in a home must be based on the unique needs of the individual. Although it takes a diplomatic and very careful approach, it is useful to make decisions regarding palliative care issues and other related matters during the early, mild stages, when the person is still able to verbalise what he or she prefers, where and how he/she wants to be at the stage when it is likely that he/she will be physically and mentally unable to cooperate in making this type of important decision. That is why early diagnosis is so important. It might seem cruel at first, talking about these matters and making plans for the far future, but this will give plenty of time for preparation and will, in the end, bring great relief to the individual.

CHAPTER
14

STIGMAS, MYTHS, FACTS

The number of people diagnosed with dementia is increasing rapidly worldwide and more than 100 different types of dementia have been identified. Statistics show that the number of young people under the age of 40 affected by the condition has grown dramatically in the last decade. It is pure speculation, but I cannot help but draw a parallel between dementia and constant drug use or chronic alcohol consumption, especially as Korsakoff's syndrome is connected with the latter.

Ignoring the problem and the disease does not make dementia disappear. Feeling ashamed and desperately trying to keep it a secret from the shop assistant and the hairdresser, or barber, does not mean that it does not exist and definitely does not mean it is easier to handle. If people have reached a stage where their dementia is obvious to others, they do not experience the rational response of realising they are ill. Instead, they see a distorted world around them. Within this false world they are unable to understand that what they say or do can sometimes be odd, annoying or irritating to other people, and most of the time they do not realise that they are living with dementia. However, there is one thing that people with this condition perceive very keenly and accurately, and that is the emotional reaction they receive from others via facial expressions or even hidden, repressed feelings.

If I took Sylvia to the local café with feelings of embarrassment, I am sure she would sense it and react accordingly. People with dementia can feel when others are embarrassed or ashamed of them. They live in fear of what people might think, of being ridiculed or being drowned in pity in public, or even worse, stigmatised as stupid or as an idiot.

People with dementia cannot live their lives in isolation like hermits. As soon as they enter into any interaction with the immediate environment, they observe the reluctance of friends or visitors to be with them, they feel the sadness of their family members when they accompany them to the GP, they see the pity in the eyes of their neighbour when they have a word over the garden fence. Little by little, people start to avoid them and on the faces of those who still talk to them, what they see is a mixture of forced kindness and compassion.

People with a severe level of dementia will not necessarily understand why they feel very down at times, or what causes their sadness; they just feel that something is not right. The feeling is precisely the same in the milder stages of the disease, only then the person affected knows exactly what causes the depression and profound sorrow. The reason why they do not want to get out of bed and why their facial expression is one of constant bitterness, is because they fear for their future, for their very being, at the mercy of this condition.

The carer's role, and that of everyone who comes into contact with people with dementia, is to break through this barricade, otherwise every person affected is in danger of ending up in a care home specialising in mental health problems or on a psychiatric ward in hospital, where they could be treated with sedatives and psychotropic drugs and could spend the rest of their life vegetating in a state of complete apathy. As a result, they could very quickly become unable to engage in any interaction with others, and could feel lonely, abandoned, isolated and bereft of all dignity, an outcome which must be avoided.

Sylvia's family, friends and people in her neighbourhood, particularly her hairdresser, are wonderful examples of exactly how to interact with a person with dementia.

I go with Sylvia to the hairdresser's once a week. It is a very short walk from her house and if we take it very slowly she can still just manage it without getting tired. Each time I have to allow extra time for our walk there and back as people say 'Hello' to Sylvia or stop for a chat about how she is and, of course, about the weather.

These short conversations are just like the ones anyone might have on meeting someone they know in the street, or coming across a friend they are glad to see. Everyone knows Sylvia well and is aware of her condition, and it is always so refreshing to see that there is nothing false or forced in their words or gestures, absolutely no sign of pity or sadness detectable in their faces.

Cornelia, Sylvia's hairstylist, gives just the right answer to everything that her lovely client says, and it is clear that she has a great understanding of both Sylvia and of dementia, which she has developed through the years they have known each other. The decline in Sylvia's condition is happening in front of her eyes, and she has heard quite a few very odd sentences coming from her client, but Cornelia never laughs at her and is careful that she only smiles with Sylvia, never at her, as she knows that everything Sylvia is saying or doing is real for her and, as far as she is concerned, totally true. She does not bat an eyelid when Sylvia asks her, 'Is my hair very dirty? You know, sweetie, it's because I've come straight from the factory, so I'd be really grateful if you could wash it twice and very thoroughly today.'

Small talk and everyday relationships like this make it possible for Sylvia to live a complete life, because she does not feel stigmatised by other people's reactions to her and she does not feel that she is being treated differently from anyone else. It does not cross her mind to stay at home or isolate herself from others, because there is nothing unpleasant or threatening in the outside world due to the unconditional and never-ending support she receives from family, friends, people in her neighbourhood and care workers, in both her micro and macro environment. The aim is to maintain Sylvia's self-confidence and emotional equilibrium for as long as possible and this should be the aim of all carers of people with dementia.

It is nowhere near enough just to avoid stigmas; much more than that is needed – namely, a better integration between wider society and those who have dementia. Public awareness must be raised in order to bring about a complete change of attitude towards the disease. A positive approach towards it is more and more evident in many Western countries, thanks in part to the media, where already a change in attitude is evident in their willingness to publicise stories, research results or the latest information about dementia care.

The tremendous efforts put into promulgating and highlighting the person-centred care approach have paid dividends in terms of getting the message across to the right people and the right places in many countries, albeit rather slowly. The more information there is about this ultimately incurable disease, the more people want to acquire this knowledge and professionalism. As a result of experience gained by caring for those with dementia and by attending courses and seminars given by practitioners, a significantly increased number of people are travelling confidently into the fascinating world of dementia. I have used the adjective 'fascinating' with good reason. As in a game of chess, by taking the right next move, it is surprising how effectively people with this condition can be helped and how their skills can be maintained and even improved.

When I managed the respite home in Australia, I arranged for all my staff to attend Dementia Simulation Training, a half-day educational workshop. This course enables attendees to experience how a person with dementia may feel while trying to complete very simple everyday tasks and I feel it should be available for everybody involved in dementia care as it is an absolutely mind-blowing and, more importantly, attitude-changing experience. It certainly opened new avenues for me when I took part in it, even though I already had detailed, high-level knowledge of this mental condition. Participants in this unique demonstration feel the real emotions, sensations and impacts that people with dementia experience every day: they feel lost, think of themselves as idiots, and experience confusion. While trying to carry out special guided exercises they endure the frustration of having their hearing hampered by strong background noise, as well as every other possible negative impact. It is extremely enlightening and genuinely enables carers to become much more aware of environmental factors, so that next time they interact with someone who has dementia, what they say or do is clear. Having this experience provides a different, more profound level of knowledge, and with this knowledge carers can eliminate most of the possible triggers that could lead to challenging, negative behaviour.

The final part of the course is a debriefing about what has happened in which every participant has the opportunity to talk about his or her personal feelings and share their experiences with the group. Talking about the barriers noticed along the way to achieving certain tasks really imprints on participants' minds exactly where mistakes might have been made in previous interactions and having experienced these difficulties in practice gives those attending the workshop a much more powerful and lasting lesson than what is heard or read about in a training manual.

The time when everybody, young, middle-aged or elderly, will understand this disease and treat those who have it in the most appropriate and successful way, is still a long way off. Yet relatively minor adjustments, such as learning new daily routines and habits, can slow decline and postpone the most severe periods of this mental condition for years, giving the person with dementia more chance to retain a dignified and relatively independent lifestyle for longer.

Myths and misunderstandings about dementia are still all too evident in the reactions of a significant part of society. These stem partly from a lack of knowledge about the disease, and partly from fear: fear of the unknown, of odd behaviour, of sometimes shocking and unexpected mood changes, of altered personalities and possible aggression.

In the years I have worked in the field of dementia, I have heard a lot of negative comments from carers, nurses and other healthcare professionals along the lines of, 'Be careful with that one, she's always trying to manipulate,' or, 'Just ignore him, he's only attention-seeking.' Even more upsetting are remarks such as, 'That idiot will keep trying to hit you; don't get too close.' These types of 'you should give up on them' opinions have always inspired me to pay extra attention to the person being referred to. Even when it is difficult to do a good, professional job in a stressful and understaffed situation, it is essential to find a way of using knowledge, skills and common sense to approach every individual with dementia in an appropriate manner.

Once a carer makes a decision to become totally committed and dedicated to dementia, it creeps into the bones and stays forever. Regardless of the environment, whether it is a care home, a respite home, day care, in-home care or helping to support a neighbour, a carer's basic principles will always be present, and, when necessary, by digging deep down into the bedrock of knowledge and experience, solutions can be found for all kinds of challenges. In all my years of working as a carer I have certainly experienced verbal aggression, but I have never been kicked or punched, although I have had to deal with a number of people with dementia in aggressive states.

Residents with dementia in one care home where I worked accepted their medication from me, regularly let me carry out complex nursing tasks such as PEG feeding (feeding through a tube directly into the stomach) or wound dressing, yet some of these residents were reputed to start throwing things as soon as someone entered their room. Other members of staff reported that they would hurl books, papers, cushions, slippers, towels, whatever was in reach at that moment. I am neither a magician nor a saint, but I think part of my success in the unique world of dementia is due to the knowledge I have gained and the person-centred practice I follow. My strategy is always to pay attention to the person with dementia, and to observe and believe the evidence of my own eyes, rather than accept any myths, stories or gossip.

Marcus was the resident in the care home who got the worst press.

The more I get to hear about Marcus, the more I feel that he is trying to communicate by throwing things. In my view he wants to demonstrate that he does not feel good, he does not like the way in which staff approach him, and perhaps the way in which care is being provided is causing him pain or discomfort.

My feeling is that his frustration and anger are naturally growing because the only reaction he notices in response to his actions is that no one is really listening to him.

I never base my practice on what others do. I stick to my own techniques as they seem to work well for me and for those with dementia in my care. I decide to try using them with Marcus.

I go to his room and follow the basic rules of courtesy. I knock on his door before I enter and wait for his permission to go in. I go to his bedside and introduce myself in a friendly way. I ask his permission to give him his medication and offer him the choice of taking it now or later. I ask his permission to clean the insertion site of his feeding tube. I take the time to complete seemingly minor, unofficial tasks, such as wiping his table clean, as its surface is always sticky from spilt tea, food and liquid medication, and ask if there is anything else I can do for him before I leave the room.

Before long, I gained Marcus's full cooperation. There was no magic or trickery on my part, quite the contrary. By showing him kindness, good manners and respect, and by treating him as a human being and giving him choices, he always did everything I asked him to. I never received a single insult from him and he never tried to throw anything at me.

Every time I visited his room, I made sure I followed the same routine and approached him as if it was our very first meeting, as the main characteristic of dementia is short-term memory loss. There is no brain capacity or ability to store new information.

It was not in Marcus's personality to be friendly and I never expected him to be, but when I was greeted by a faint smile, hardly visible, months later, that was like a prize or award for me. That was all the positive feedback I needed as it showed me that what I had been doing was right and good for him.

■ ■ ■

In an ideal, dementia-friendly world, everybody – shop assistants, newsagents, postmen or women, pharmacists – would have a basic level of understanding of dementia, its signs and symptoms, and the different ways of managing communication with people who are affected. Anyone living with dementia would feel safe to go out and they would not necessarily need a guardian with them, as everybody around would be a friend, or a friendly face, a helper who would always have a smile and be able to give that little 'push' when needed. If, for instance, they forgot where they had wanted to go, there would always be someone who would try to find out by patiently asking direct, simple questions. People with dementia would be able to go out to buy milk, post their letters and do everyday small things that we all do independently without any trouble. Within their local community it would be impossible to get lost, because everybody would know where they lived and there would be someone on every corner who would give directions, or accompany them home.

This description of a dementia-friendly world where people living with the condition can do things by themselves, and where the environment almost invisibly protects them with lots of love and support, offers what I call quality of life. It seems a utopian ideal, but there are increasingly encouraging reports about local communities where this is a reality and entire villages are involved in dementia care, for example in Japan and in the Netherlands.

I feel that, by working in in-home care, I can most closely replicate on a small scale what, until recently, I believed to be naïve thoughts about a dementia-friendly world. When I look at Sylvia, even though she is in a late stage of dementia, I see a physically fit elderly woman, who is dressed with style, who moves around the house or in her micro environment confidently, even when she is wandering; a person who enjoys moments in life such as sitting by the river or going out for a drive like anybody else. The reason she looks and feels that way is because she has a discreet helping hand with her that she can grasp in difficult times; but when everything is going well, and she does not need anything, that hand is held back and lets her live her life the way she chooses.

It is not unusual at all for Sylvia to ask me nicely to leave her alone for a while. At first she said this quite often, but I soon learnt to read the signs that meant she wanted a little time on her own: peace and quiet without anybody around her. Allowing people with dementia time on their own is as important a part of dementia care as changing pads, or telling them the right date or time.

The objective is to build a strong trusting relationship between the carer and the person being cared for. This relationship can develop into a friendship, as it has done with Sylvia, but whatever the relationship, a carer should never expect appreciation. Once in a blue moon Sylvia might say something like, 'Thank you for being so kind, I don't know what would I do without you,' but the aim of my work is to ensure that she is not aware of being cared for and the feedback that shows how successful this aim has been is precisely the fact that, most of the time, she shows no gratitude. Of course, she says 'Thank you' a lot – for example, when I serve lunch or pick up something from the floor that she has just dropped – but never usually for my care work, and that is how it should be. She sees me as a friend who is visiting and staying with her for a while, with whom she has a very good relationship, and who is involved in family matters such as birthdays, Christmas and Easter; someone who answers her questions without judgement or ridicule, and who encourages her day by day to be herself.

I cannot stress too strongly that the only approach to the world of dementia is through the person, as an individual, and not through generalisation. All the successes in my entire career to date are due to person-centred care and a person-centred attitude and, never mind how many different people with dementia I have cared for, I still begin every new placement by being full of openness and curiosity to learn about the particular person I have come to care for. I believe that even in the advanced stages of the disease, people are able to communicate, if not with words, with actions and non-verbal communication, signalling to me somehow that what is happening to them is good or unpleasant. It is up to carers to observe these signals and to decide what can be done about them by defining the trigger, and ascertaining whether it has an emotional or a physiological origin.

I do not believe in myths. It is pure myth that there is nothing much that can be done with people who have severe dementia or that they are unable to make contact with their environment. This is simply not true.

These people are open to creative ideas, they react to the kindness and attention they receive and they like leisure time and entertaining activities, just like anybody else. It all comes down to the one simple question carers must answer before they start: 'How much time and patience do you have to provide proper care for people with dementia?'

Although the details of small pleasures and happy moments might be forgotten in a few seconds, minutes or hours, the feelings and emotions triggered last much longer, helping carers to keep the spirits of people with the condition in balance and to support their general well-being. The focus must be on what they can still do and not on what they are no longer able to do, on skills that they continue to be able to employ in ways that make them happy, such as reading a book, listening to music, gardening, sewing, cleaning, cooking, playing board games, playing the piano, participating in activities with others, doing exercise and, more recently, using the internet and playing computer games. The list is endless. When people are involved in activities they like, the transformation is visible, their faces come alive and negative thoughts are banished in the blink of an eye.

When I was responsible for running the dementia-focused programme in the respite home I mentioned earlier, I successfully applied for funding to buy an entertainment console, including a large-screen LCD TV, a Wii console with all the equipment needed to play videogames, and a DVD player. In my application I remember highlighting the fact that it can be highly stimulating for someone living with dementia to be able to play different sports while sitting safely in a chair.

The console proved to be very successful with many of our residents and the investment was definitely worthwhile. Darts, tennis, different Olympic events, strategy games, fun quizzes – we had them all. Helpers were always on hand to explain briefly and simply the aims of the different activities, the rules, how to do the activities and to help out if the residents got stuck. It was incredible to see how quickly many elderly people with dementia could learn how to use the different tools and features on the console. They bravely tried various different sports and were completely open to new experiences.

Of course, residents could not remember information from previous occasions so each time they were encouraged to use the console again, a carer went through the introduction and training as if for the first time.

For me, this is one of the many charms of the condition: carers repeat themselves at least as many times as do people who have dementia!

Witnessing people with this condition blossoming, observing a room filled with laughter and positive energy, seeing the sparkle in people's eyes, feeling the unconditional love and happiness experienced by those taking part, and knowing that you have made a large contribution to this is a carer's privilege. By using the games console, people with dementia benefited from a unique leisure opportunity that left pleasant emotions despite the residents' short-term memory loss. If nothing else, they remembered the positive feeling they had in relation to the respite home the next time they returned. People living with dementia might not know what happened to them in a particular place, they might not remember a single detail, but they know that, for some reason, they love coming back.

■ ■ ■

CHAPTER
15

SHATTERED MINDS

It is not at all my intention to portray dementia care as an inspiring vocation where there are solutions for every problem or challenge, where all changes in the behaviour of people with the condition are manageable, and where every word they say makes sense when translated by a dictionary in our head that gives meaning to their every sentence and action. This is not the case.

When you choose this profession, or find yourself in the position of a carer, you must take into account that sometimes you will need to move mountains in order to reach your goals successfully, and an enormous amount of energy, way beyond what would be considered normal, will be required. The honest truth is that it is physically and mentally hard work, with very limited opportunities for breaks or rest.

As a live-in carer, unless you have a complete break from your work when someone else is in charge, you never 'switch off'. Even then, if you have built up a close relationship with the person you are caring for, their welfare is always on your mind. Yet, while it is exhausting being an effective guide through this messy, at first sight even frightening, labyrinth, the carer also gains a great deal: not only knowledge and experience, but also love and positive recognition, mostly coming from the family and friends of the person with dementia, which recharge the batteries instantly when energy levels get low. These are the chief resources that help to maintain a healthy balance, which is what keeps the 'big wheel' in motion.

Unfortunately, Sylvia will never be as she was before dementia. However, as a result of having me, or any of my colleagues, living with her, she has a chance to lead a relatively normal life regardless of her mental impairment. Looking at her life from her perspective, it seems happy and satisfying.

One of the hardest things when dealing with a broken mind is to prevent boredom. Sometimes it takes me a long time to find the right activity for Sylvia, the one that makes her happy and that she enjoys doing at that particular moment, as what engages Sylvia's attention changes day by day.

Mostly Sylvia is unable to express what she would like to do, but at times she verbalises a strong wish to do something, yet it is often as irrational as 'going to school', or something she believes she can still do that in reality would be impossible for her at her advanced stage of dementia, such as going back to studying or to work. Unaware of her disorientation in time or place, she insists on sending me out to get notebooks for school, to pick up a brochure from the local college with listings of upcoming courses and the start dates of the new terms, or to buy some pearl-headed dressmaking pins.

If Sylvia gets the idea that she must return to work and it does not happen immediately, it hurts her deeply. I never argue with comments such as, 'They haven't even bothered to pick up the phone and call me. They're obviously just jealous as everybody knows I'm the best.' I am too busy trying to find a way to distract her from her upsetting thoughts.

Such disappointments can easily give rise to depression or feelings that life is worthless, even if the disappointment is self-generated and based on a false sense of reality. These situations demand action and it is the carer's responsibility to find something to fill the void and lead the person with dementia back to the present.

Distractions such as reading and watching television are always on hand, but increasingly they are only effective for a limited time as they are tiring both for the eyes and for the mind. As tiredness and confusion grow, people with this condition lose the ability to concentrate and eventually lose interest in these activities.

Taking a person with dementia out into the outside world is an ideal distraction if it is possible. Reality has a strong impact on Sylvia when we go out to public places, such as cafés, parks or supermarkets. She is always completely engaged during grocery shopping, for instance, holding the handle of the trolley and slowly walking up and down the aisles. She wants to know if I have a shopping list, gives serious consideration to the merits of two different brands of the same product when I ask for her opinion, listens when I explain exactly what the product is that I have just put into the trolley and what I will use it for, and why we have to wait in the queue at the check-out. I have never heard her complain or criticise while we were shopping; after all, we have a mission and she has an important and very useful part in it.

People like to be needed. At times when Sylvia's lethargy is about to take over, I pretend I need her help. Helping to prepare lunch is an example I have given already, but it can be just a small thing, like explaining the meaning of an English word that I pretend I do not know. As long as I ask her to help with something she perceives she can do, her self-esteem is strengthened and her spirits raised.

People also like to be able to give support to those less fortunate than themselves and when Sylvia's behaviour starts to indicate that she is about to go completely off kilter, I suddenly find a reason to make her feel sorry for me. It brings out her mother instinct.

Sylvia is doing the crossword. In her own way, of course. She is writing everything down that comes to mind, completely ignoring the numbers and spaces, or the possible letters that would fit.

Watching her from a distance, it looks as if she is really thinking it through, putting the right answers in and seriously working on the correct solution. 'Bloody this' and 'bloody that' are part of the performance and she blames anything and anybody but herself if she cannot think of the right word. As she gets more and more agitated, she starts telling unconnected stories, making absolutely no sense whatsoever.

Suddenly she turns to me and asks: 'What is the name of that bloody seabird that lives in Antarctica?'

My time has come! I seize the opportunity.

'I wish I knew, Sylvia, but I am not as good as you are at crosswords. They take more intelligence than I've got, I'm sorry. I'm not the right person to help you in a clever thing like a crossword.'

My exaggerated foolishness and self-deprecating words hit the target. I notice an instant change in her facial expression and attitude. In a flash Sylvia switches from being offensive to supportive; even her swearing vanishes for a while and the atmosphere in the room suddenly and noticeably changes to being pleasant and positive. Sylvia feels that she can take the lead, so she puts her upsetting thoughts aside and tries to help me, the weaker, more vulnerable person.

Making myself out to be less intelligent than I am is a small sacrifice in order to bring us both back some peace.

A carer is just like a clever small-time detective, always keeping an eye open for the little details that reveal a lot about someone's mood and for the signs that indicate that a change is about to occur. One of the golden rules in dementia care is finding and removing the trigger for difficult behaviour so that normal balance can be maintained or restored.

When I was in charge of the respite home and on call, I received an emergency phone call from a staff member on duty asking if I could help with a new admission. A gentleman with severe dementia who had never been parted from his wife of 50 years was clearly rejecting the idea of spending a few days at the respite home while his wife went to visit family members. He was refusing to go into the house, no matter how much reassurance was given by the carer, and insisted on waiting by the fence with his suitcase until his wife got back.

Slowing down to drive through the electric gate I can hear the man shouting. He is calling out to pedestrians, asking for help, saying that he is a prisoner and begging them to rescue him.

I decide not to waste time by trying to persuade him that all the staff are really nice or that the home is warm and welcoming inside. I know that, given his age, he must be very tired as he has been standing there for quite a while, so my first 'snake charming' action is to bring out one chair for him and one for myself. I put them down next to each other.

I sit down on one of the chairs and wait.

He watches me suspiciously. After a few minutes he sits down on the other chair.

We sit in companionable silence. Finally he starts talking to me and we begin a pleasant conversation. He has calmed down completely now and gradually starts to tell me about his fears and doubts. I listen attentively, only saying a few words when it is absolutely necessary.

It is getting noticeably colder and darker as evening approaches. By this time, we have made a connection and I am no longer a stranger to him, so I offer him a cup of tea in the house. He gladly agrees, picks up his suitcase and walks with me to the front door.

As we go in, I introduce him to the staff and residents as my friend who is visiting, and he shakes hands with the other two men who are staying with us.

I make sure he is settled in before I return home.

During our life together I have drawn up a long mental list of all Sylvia's triggers, and keep a constant lookout for the involuntary signals and clues Sylvia gives that indicate discomfort or distress. I know when she is experiencing physical discomfort, when I need to turn her hearing aid down, when she needs to go to the toilet, when her clothes are uncomfortable, when she is getting tired or hungry.

One day soon after my arrival, I made sure that lunch would be ready in the oven on our return from a short walk in the country as I knew that we would both be hungry. I was so ravenous that I finished my meal before Sylvia had made much progress with hers. As soon as I stopped eating, she put her cutlery down on the table, and even though her plate was still full of food, she would not continue eating. Until she agreed to have some biscuits with her tea later, low blood sugar levels meant that the afternoon was an endurance test for us both. When we sat down for dinner, I decided to try an experiment. Again I bolted my food and finished first, but this time I pretended I was still eating by making noises on the empty plate with my knife and fork. It worked! Sylvia carried on eating. I had eliminated the trigger that was stopping her finishing her meal because of her need to satisfy her notion of good table manners.

I have learnt to understand what triggers her emotional distress too, but there are days when she likes to complain about and criticise everything and it seems as if she is looking for a reason to be sad. Sometimes being grumpy, argumentative, uncooperative, stubborn and constantly saying 'no' seems to bring her some relief and temporary satisfaction and I have become convinced that one of the reasons for this kind of behaviour is that she is attention-seeking. She wants to get me involved so that I can solve the problem for her. For healthy minds, it is a simple matter to confront whatever is causing the problem and find some possible logical solutions, but this is impossible for those living with advanced dementia.

I can tell that Sylvia is delving deeply into her presumed sorrows again, so I offer her the opportunity to go out and treat ourselves to a coffee somewhere followed by window shopping. As always, I back up my verbal communication by actions showing that we are about to go out. I get my handbag and start to put on my 'going out' shoes.

I can almost see the cogs in Sylvia's damaged brain turning, as, as I expected, she tries to find a polite excuse to refuse my invitation so that she can continue with her complaints.

'I wish I could go, sweetie, but the GP said I must stay in and rest when the weather is as cold as it is today. You know, at my age there might be serious consequences if I catch a cold or flu.'

'Maybe another time,' I reply commiseratingly and then add, 'It would be terrible if you caught something nasty; it's not worth it.'

Outside the temperature is 23 degrees.

My validation of her excuse calms Sylvia down. She becomes quiet and peaceful, and looks at the paper for a short while before taking a nap in her comfy armchair. Then I know that her inner calm is restored.

Carers must never forget, even for a moment, that the mental conditions classed as dementia destroy the brain. Emotionally it can be very draining to care for someone who has dementia, but a carer must always bear in mind that it is not the fault of the person with dementia, and that there are moments when the mind actually stops working and disintegrates because of the disease. Just because the behaviour of a person with dementia may be a little odd, it does not necessarily mean that anything has to be done about it. Action is only required when the challenging behaviour becomes potentially harmful for the person with the condition or for others. A carer has to get used to strange, sometimes bizarre, events when living with people who have this problem.

Reasoned argument and sensible explanation cannot be used with people with dementia. It is a hugely challenging task to lead someone out of their hallucinations and paranoia, someone who can no longer see the difference between right and wrong, truth or falsehood, real and imaginary. It is an even greater task to give that person support with a smiling face and without making him or her feel he or she is unwell or uncared for.

I have come up against the feeling, especially when I first started working as a carer, that if I did not give up at that precise moment, I too would go mad and be in urgent need of rescue myself.

Sylvia is not aware – and she should not be – that her behaviour is sometimes so irritating and challenging that I would like to scream or cry. I have learnt to keep these emotions hidden from her and I have certainly developed greater tolerance during the long time I have spent with her. However, continuously suppressing anger and frustration does take its toll and I confess that there are moments when I get close to breaking point, just a millimetre away from nervous collapse, when I feel that my patience and energy are exhausted and that it is no longer possible for me to be the guide, the clever person who is able to defuse situations.

The quick fix of regular 'me time' has already been mentioned and I have developed my own technique to help me ease my mind which takes only a matter of seconds if I feel I am close to exploding point. When Sylvia follows me to my room almost instantly after I have left her, I still have responsibility for her. I must hide my anger and temper, be able to give her answers and talk to her in a voice that shows her that everything is perfectly all right before I can persuade her to leave me alone for the short time I need on my own in order to be able to relax.

I used to feel guilty about the times when I feel near breaking point, but gaining further knowledge and personal experience have helped me to realise that this is a natural reaction; it does not mean I am a bad carer. It happens to everyone and carers need to learn how to cope with this feeling of guilt by realising that they are not to blame. The strangeness, the stubbornness, and the confusion which are created by the false reality and the monotonous repetitiveness of dementia will always be there. There will be times when a mind is so shattered that it has almost disappeared and stops working. It is only when someone who understands the problem can step in and give that 'push' to help the mind through the dead point that a situation can be improved.

Although it is best for carers never to let their negative feelings show to the person with dementia, it is important to stress again that it is essential for carers to have the support of close friends or family members with whom they can share their problems and emotions when they are feeling close to the edge. Ideally these people should be from outside the circle of dementia, as they will have a fresh perspective and an outsider point of view that eventually will help the carer to get through the crisis.

Breaking points do not happen every day, of course, but no matter what a carer does, there are some occasions when nothing works – the person with dementia has got out of bed on the wrong side. When this happens, the best a carer can do is to just put up with it and carry on. Sooner or later a better day will come and things will get back to normal mode for both the carer and the cared-for. Sylvia and I have been through quite a few bad days together and I have assumed many more are yet to come, but I have kept going and continued to love doing my care work. The good news is that you will survive.

Caring for someone who has this disease is difficult, regardless of whether the carer is a professional or a family member. Frustration becomes a perfectly normal emotional reaction arising from the daily problems which are part of the very nature of this mental impairment. While a few of the most annoying characteristics, habits or events will become part of the carer's ordinary everyday life, they can occasionally arrive in droves, when the carer will face, and need to deal with, an unusual, entirely unexpected, series of events.

The consequences of repressing constant frustration, anger and exhaustion are serious and they can cause actual harm to the carer's well-being. As the level of stress increases, if the carer does not learn how to deal with it, it will damage the immune system and leave a door wide open for viruses and infections to step in. It is crucial that carers protect themselves, and ultimately the person they are caring for, by detecting the early signs of fatigue and the need for a break. Decreasing patience, aggressive thoughts towards people with dementia, inability to hide anger, crying, or physiological changes such as the sudden onset of compulsive eating, insomnia, an upset stomach, shortness of breath or frequent headaches all indicate that a break is necessary.

At such times it usually helps to stop for a minute and sort the issues into two groups – namely, the things the carer has control over, and those that the carer can do nothing about. It leads to unnecessary disappointment when a carer tries to change something that is entirely unchangeable. A carer meets several issues of that type in the field of dementia: aimless wandering, repeated questions or statements, a psychotic state, incomplete sentences, basically anything that derives from the individual's ill mind or from his or her personality – a carer has to accept the fact that the personality of the person with dementia cannot be changed.

However, there is one significant thing that can be changed and adjusted, and that is the carer's own reactions and responses to each different challenge and situation. What you say and what you do are things that you have power over. Being stuck in a 'I hate you so much' state for too long is dangerous, because it becomes ever harder to get away from permanent bitterness. If a carer recognises the warning signs it is much easier to take action to make them disappear, or at least to decrease stress and frustration to a level where they are bearable.

Everyone's way of doing this is different. It is something carers have to experiment with to find out what works best for them. As I have already explained, I like to get away for a short period of time and my usual excuse is that I need to go to the loo. Some people listen to music or pray, for example. Doing deep breathing exercises is a physical way to help relieve acute stress and even focusing on care work paperwork to distract the mind for a while is effective. It can be anything really, but the point is that any one of these useful techniques will ultimately help carers see the problem more objectively and keep control over how they respond to it.

Whether you are a carer, family member or friend of someone living with dementia, I can guarantee that you will come to the point when you have to force yourself to think of their loveable qualities, the things that you find most attractive about them, and, when you do, I promise it will make everything much easier. Instead of concentrating on negative thoughts, I often summarise the things that I love about Sylvia. For instance, I have tremendous respect for all the things she has done and achieved in life. When she is in a good mood, her sense of humour is priceless, right up my street: a little witty, a little absurd but always just the thing to make me laugh every time. This is a real blessing in dementia care. Considering her age and the advanced stage of dementia she has reached, the knowledge she has retained in certain areas and the fact that she still uses words and short sentences from the different languages she used to speak fluently is incredible. I truly admire her and over the three and a half years I have known her, I have learnt a lot from her.

It is always worthwhile stepping aside from the frustrating situation for a second before doing or saying something that you might later regret and feel ashamed of. This would leave a deeper mark in people with dementia than many might think. If you are a full-time carer and family member, it might be useful to seek out other families nearby in similar circumstances, so you could sometimes swap over responsibilities and give each other a break for a few hours. Just being in a different environment can make a difference. In my view it is much harder to look after a close relative and I have noticed that I, as a professional, can do things that family would not be able to do. I treat Sylvia differently, and she accepts things from me that she would not accept from a family member. Being too involved makes care work more difficult.

Dedication, willingness and determination are essential virtues required for doing this kind of work correctly and over a long period. At more pessimistic times (I am glad to say these are rarer and briefer for me now) all carers feel 'Anybody could do what I do' and at others, that they are not good enough. Carers must learn how to turn these negative feelings into something positive. Remember, everyone has faults and no one is perfect regardless of their mental capacity. I have been working with people with dementia for years now, but I still ask myself at the end of each day: 'Would I do everything in the same way again?' In some instances the answer is 'No', and thanks to my constant analysis of events I often find a better way of dealing with a particular situation next time it occurs. When I see the new, improved approach working better, the feeling I experience is indescribable.

Of course I do not believe that only I and a few elite others in this world can provide dementia care of the highest possible standard. I do believe, however, that this kind of care work does not suit everybody. I know several people who have tried working as carers but who then had to admit that they could not make all the necessary and unavoidable compromises needed. At this point I feel I should make a personal confession: if you choose to do live-in care, in my view you have to subordinate many things in your personal life in order to be able to do it properly. I know this may sound very tough to many people, but this is how I manage. As far as I am concerned, this is not a great sacrifice as the immense satisfaction I gain from my work, together with the feeling that I am doing something extraordinarily worthwhile, far outweighs anything that I have to give up.

As a result of this type of care work, my knowledge of the nature of dementia has deepened and expanded into unexpected dimensions and my thinking is now much more about solutions than about problems. As far as behaviour is concerned, over the years I have been working in this field, I have experienced and dealt with some extreme examples, so I now feel confident in saying that I understand and speak the language of dementia. As time goes by, I feel more and more comfortable in this unique world. In fact, quite often when I take a break away from my care work, I find I have less patience with 'normal' people than I have with those who have a mental condition. It appears that the world of people with dementia has become more predictable and peaceful for me than the real world, as there is no ill will, even in the most challenging behaviour. These lovely people give their love and smile unconditionally, they never manipulate or cheat, or at least that is never their principal intention, whereas the real, 'normal' world is full of unpleasant behaviour.

All it takes is for me to see someone jump a queue, overhear a loud argument, or witness a childish battle for supremacy on the road, and immediately I wish to be back in the innocent world of dementia, back with Sylvia, who recently said quietly to me: 'Thank you.'

'What for?' I asked her.

'For everything you do for me.'

■ ■ ■

- When Sylvia believes I am her sister and treats me as family,
- When she asks for my help because she trusts me and knows I can solve the problem,
- When she says 'Goodnight' and grasps my hands saying: 'Promise me you will still be here in the morning',
- When she cries if she sees me leaving with a suitcase,
- When she apologises for something she has done, cannot recall exactly what it was, but just feels something is wrong and she wants to make it up to me,
- When I see joy shining in her eyes,
- When her family calls me 'Saint Agnes' ...

For moments like these, I say it is worth being there a thousand times over, helping to hold together the pieces of a shattered mind.

■ ■ ■

CHAPTER
16

SELF-ASSESSMENT

In the course of my memorable journey through the special world of dementia, it is not only the behaviour of the people with dementia that I analyse on the way. I also regularly do self-assessments which provide a useful, and, as I have found, a quite unexpected bonus to my work.

Very early on in my work as a carer I realised that I have to be grateful even for the tough days and moments, because having experienced them, I am certainly more aware of how I live my own life. Since I started this chapter of my career, I have tried to get the best reactions out of myself in a crisis as well as in different everyday routine situations, and I realise that my behaviour is now far less unpredictable than it used to be. With comparatively little effort I can now exercise significantly more control over everything I do and over everything that I help people with dementia to do.

I have learnt to know the tone of voice that works best if Sylvia is panicking because she believes her handbag has been stolen. I know the exact words I need to use if I want her to take her pills three times a day. What I have found works really well is if I treat anything that I know full well she does not want to do – like taking her pills – as a mere nothing, a sort of 'by the way' task that does not deserve more attention than, in this case, a pill she quickly pops into her mouth after I've put it into her hand, followed by a drink of water. Even though I turn my back on her while she is doing this to emphasise that taking a pill really is nothing, I keep an eye on her actions and check carefully to see that she has swallowed her medication. Although her care notes emphasised that she had a history of being difficult over taking her tablets, with me, she has never refused to take them.

It took countless conflicts and periods of challenging behaviour for me to understand that Sylvia's aggression was often linked to me and that I was generating it. Initially I was annoyed by her unpredictable reactions, I said the wrong thing, I raised my voice, I grimaced involuntarily, I did not invest enough time and ingenuity in identifying the right form of distraction, I started to believe that she was doing things on purpose to make my life miserable and so I pressed all the wrong buttons. Now in similar difficult situations it only takes me a fraction of a second to be able to stand back, take an objective view, identify if I am the cause of the stress and recognise what I have done or said to generate her agitation. All I have to do is to keep observing her reactions, which, like a mirror, reflect whether my care at that moment is right or whether we have a hitch.

Conscious of the heavy weight of responsibility that rests on my shoulders because my actions and words have a strong influence on Sylvia's life every day, I have had to reach an advanced level of self-control and consciously chosen conduct which, before becoming a carer, I did not believe I was capable of. My family say that looking after people with dementia has made me a better person, and I am sure that in doing this type of work, all carers have an invaluable opportunity to find and develop their finest traits and improve their personalities.

I am always discreet and talk in generalities, but there are times when my close friends and family are aware that I have had an exceptionally hard day. I know that the advice I receive is meant to be encouraging, but if I put the impractical and drastic ideas sometimes suggested into practice I know that Sylvia would only become more confused and therefore more agitated as a result, and that she would then ultimately sap the nervous strength of even the strongest mind, until physical or mental breaking point is reached. People may say things like 'I've no idea how you handle these things. If I were you, I would have given up, that's for sure.' But I have no intention of giving up.

The only viable approach in caring for a person with dementia is very simple, but nonetheless valid: what you must do is only to provide care in the way that you would like to receive it yourself if you were in a similar situation. That is why the Dementia Simulation Training mentioned earlier is so useful, because it demonstrates real feelings and gives an accurate insight into the day-to-day lives of people with this mental condition. Frustration, feelings of emptiness and being useless, agitation or aggression cannot be treated by adding more stress, ridicule, rudeness or disparagement. I often think of the carer of someone with dementia as an actor in the theatre. The audience expects actors to leave their personal problems and troubles to one side when they step onto the stage. All an audience is interested in is seeing the performance, the play, and does not need to know that the actor broke up with her lover earlier that afternoon, or that his flat was repossessed as he could not pay the monthly mortgage.

Just like an actor stepping on stage, I have to leave my own problems and feelings behind as soon as I enter the home of a person with dementia. Naturally, I have as many unsolved problems, pending tasks and pressing concerns as any other human being, not least among them being the emotional effects of being separated from my family for long periods and not always being able to attend important celebrations such as birthdays or Christmas. I have lived through emotional highs and lows where sometimes only tears can bring sweet relief both physically and mentally.

Sylvia knows nothing of this of course. If she saw me crying or being sad in a situation that she could not connect to a particular event, it would cause total confusion in her already damaged mind. She relies on me to be her rock, that steady, permanent point that is predictable and strong in order to give her strength as well as boundless support and stability. When the darkest side of dementia strikes Sylvia, I scroll forward in my mind from the current scenario and play events through from my own point of view. What would I like to hear now, what would calm me down, what would really help to reduce my anger, assuage my disappointment or ease my fears? In challenging situations, I draw on my bank of personal solutions as well as all the well-known, tried and tested techniques in order to solve the problem, and fortunately there is usually a cure. Then I do exactly the same when the next problem occurs.

There is one thing in care work that I can guarantee, and it is that after a while you will come to a point where you feel everything is unfair. Unfair in that you have responsibility for the actions and well-being of someone who has a mental condition and has no idea what they are doing or why. Unfair because they can change their behaviour from one moment to the next without any consequences and you may not. They are allowed to wake up at night, to wander around, then have a lovely snooze during the day, and you are not able to do any of these things. They have the freedom and free will to do whatever they wish, while you do not have all these rights.

As with many things in life, a carer just has to have to have the right mental attitude. You must think clearly and see if you are (or are not) ready to help somebody out of their predicament. Unlike the person who has dementia, you have the mental capacity to decide if you are capable of doing this or not, and that decision needs to be made before you agree to undertake this type of care work.

I often wonder what I would do if one day someone said to me, 'I'm afraid I have bad news for you. You have dementia.' How would I react if suddenly I found myself in the shoes of someone with dementia? After so many years of dealing with this particular mental condition, I have some idea of what sort of crucial information should be provided to my future carer so that I would be able to receive a person-centred approach and continue a high quality of life. Those unfortunate people who reach an advanced stage of dementia without having been given a diagnosis or any appropriate support, lack the opportunity to offer their carers a guide to their likes and dislikes, habits and hobbies, details of their life history or an important overview of their personality.

In these cases, the carer has to gather the information from second-hand sources. Yet even if it comes from close family members and friends, this information can sometimes be mistaken – there can be intimate details and very personal dreams that a daughter might not necessarily know about her mother, or a son about his father. Some information is better than nothing of course, but the picture given by family or friends can be subjective as it is based on their perspective of their loved one's life. During my professional life as a carer I have met cases where details provided about a relative with dementia represented more what the family wanted to see in that person, rather than reality.

These mismatches could be just minor details about a person that, it turns out later, do not quite add up when the carer gets to know the person with dementia better – a skilled carer notices the truth by reading the reactions and behaviour of the person affected.

According to information given by his family, one man that I looked after with the disease loved playing a particular card game. However, every time I brought up the subject of playing, my suggestion was never met with any enthusiasm and whenever I tried to play the game with him, there was no doubt that he did not enjoy the activity. After countless fruitless attempts to engage him in what I had understood was something he liked doing, he tried to verbalise his feelings and I came to realise that he had only played the game because everybody else in the family liked to play. It was the shared family activity he had enjoyed, not the game itself.

Knowing the critical importance of first-hand information in the creation of the best possible care plan for successful care giving, I decided to make my own list of things that I believe are essential if I ever become affected by dementia, or have any reduction in my mental capacity. It is a small piece of card that I keep in my purse, just in case, and it gives details of who I am, what my likes and dislikes are, my personality, which particular things could be triggers of stress, and other similar hints and facts about me.

It is a bit like the medical bracelet, jewellery or ID card that people with specific health conditions such as epilepsy or diabetes are encouraged to wear or have with them at all times.* In the event of an emergency, this saves valuable time for medical staff as it contains all the important personal information they need. If someone is unconscious, the correct treatment can still be given – the information can ultimately save the person's life.

Drawing a parallel between the use of basic life-saving medical information and that provided for dementia care is quite deliberate. Just imagine how much seemingly inexplicable agitation could be avoided by giving the care that accurately meets the needs of the person with dementia. Instead of the carer guessing and trying various things out,

---

* Alzheimer's Society UK produces a document called 'This is me' that aims to fulfil this role and is widely used in care homes and hospitals.

the person with dementia would be treated in exactly the right way to restore their happiness and equilibrium. This is why I have made my own 'dementia card', even though I secretly hope that I will never have to use it.

If I ever do need it and if my list lands in the right hands, whoever is responsible for me will know that I have to have a shower every morning. I really hate washing my hair myself, but I do not mind if a hairdresser does it for me. I like to watch particular films and TV programmes, especially a series from my childhood, as well as listen to music from my personal collection. I drink coffee not tea and I prefer to have my laptop near me all the time. I love having my family around me, and Betty, a dear friend, always has a calming effect on me, not only because of her serene personality but her songlike voice too. I like good quality plain dark chocolate, never milk or white, I am very choosy about the shoes I wear and I must have my unwanted hair on my face removed from time to time. Idle prattle makes me agitated, I like going outside whatever the weather and I am generally an introverted personality who cannot stand being the focus of attention.

When the day comes that my cognitive functions and short-term memory let me down, when people around me think I am confused and odd, when I can no longer think logically, I know that with the help of my 'dementia card', I have an excellent chance of receiving care that is based on a thorough understanding of me and my condition, care that maximises my quality of life and my happiness. I can guarantee that a carer acting appropriately on this information will make me more cooperative in completing tasks and routines, and that this will ultimately make things easier, and therefore much more pleasant, for both me and my carer. I also regard this list as a sort of solemn undertaking that if I am treated as a human being by people with a real understanding of who I am and what is happening to me, I will be a manageable, lovable person, even if I am living with dementia.

Thinking ahead and realising that it will not be long before my generation reaches the high-risk age for dementia, I have a vision of myself in a care home, surrounded by my laptop, iPad, iPod, smartphone, and goodness knows how many other similar digital tools, as all are essential parts of my life at the moment. People of my age are accustomed to daily use of the internet, belong to several different social networks and date through matchmaking websites. Using these tools would have to be part of my care plan, because these activities make me happy, they are what I am interested in, and they keep me busy and sane.

However, this raises a number of questions as far as safety and invasion of privacy are concerned. If, out of respect for my dignity and my right to a good quality of life, I were allowed to continue being online whenever I wanted, but yet had a diseased, poorly functioning mind that made me confused and disturbed, who would make sure I was safe, and check all my online activity in order to prevent the potentially catastrophic consequences of the activities of fraudsters, cheats and scoundrels? Would carers have the time or the authority to do this?

At the moment, when the people with dementia who I care for want to be alone, they usually read books, listen to music, have a nap or watch television. Considering generation X (born: 1966–1976, current population 41 million), generation Y (born: 1977–1994, current population 71 million) and generation Z (born: 1995-2012, population 23 million and growing rapidly when William J. Schroer wrote his article in 2008)[14] it is unlikely that they would be satisfied with such old-fashioned ways to relax. They will need all the tools they have been used to throughout their lives in order to remain as close as possible to the emotional and mental selves they used to be before the onset of dementia.

The changes in dementia care that will need to be implemented for generations X, Y and Z must be addressed now. As the digital era continues to have an ever-increasing effect worldwide on people's lives, all the problems that are likely to be encountered in the near future must be taken into account. People with dementia are already very vulnerable physically, emotionally and financially. If the dangers of the virtual world are added to these vulnerabilities, there is no doubt that these present a problem which demands immediate attention.

∎ ∎ ∎

CHAPTER
17

FAREWELL

I am looking at Sylvia lying in her room at home on the multifunctional hospital bed supplied by social services. She seems calm and comfortable on the pressure relief mattress that detects any part of her body that has not moved for a certain period of time and instantly alleviates the pressure on it. She is clutching the rosary I gave her a couple of days ago and it seems to give her great comfort to hold it.

Everybody around Sylvia – including myself – had been impressed, when weak but still just managing to sit in her armchair, she had commented on the handsomeness of the man who had intruded into her home in order to replace her king-sized bed with this smaller but absolutely invaluable hospital bed, that would be essential for her comfort in her final days.

The rapid decline in Sylvia's condition first became noticeable six months ago, when she suddenly had serious difficulties in using her spoon effectively when her favourite soup was served for lunch. Not only was she unable to spoon up the liquid, but she also accepted my offer of help and basically let me feed her.

I knew instantly that something was happening to her brain. Her pride and very strong sense of independence would never usually have allowed me to assist her. From that day on, she had to be fed every time any food contained liquid that needed to be eaten with a spoon, such as the cereal with milk that she usually had for breakfast.

Sylvia also started to use her hands to eat solid food, instead of her knife and fork. No matter how many different tactics I used, or how many different approaches I tried in order to lead her back to her previously lifetime-lasting routines, I had to accept the fact that she was not able to use cutlery anymore, so I adjusted my care routine to her current needs immediately.

At one point, Sylvia had to be admitted to hospital for a week for a UTI. (These are very common in people with dementia and can rapidly become severe.) Understandably, medical and nursing staff are not usually particularly happy to have someone with her condition on a non-dementia-specific ward, especially in an advanced stage. People with dementia demand too much of their time, patience, attention, kindness and understanding.

However, the fact that I stayed with Sylvia for twelve hours each day and when I went back to Sylvia's house, Linda took over from me, meant that Sylvia was the most popular patient in the whole building. Everybody loved her!

Thanks to the constant reassuring presence of Linda or me, Sylvia was cooperative during all the medical examinations, let the nurses take her blood pressure and her temperature, and even allowed a canula to be inserted into the back of her hand so that blood samples could be taken from her regularly. She talked when she wanted to, ate when she felt like it, listened to music when she was in the mood to do so, or visited the hospital café if she was up to going on a short outing.

It was necessary to explain to Sylvia several times a day where she was and why, but both Linda and I had the time, patience and understanding to give this information as many times as she needed it, together with a constant supply of smiles. As a result, Sylvia felt as if she was at home, her mental and emotional balance was steady and stress free. The thought of escaping from her hospital room was the last thing on her mind. It may sound a little bizarre, but there is no doubt that she was happy there.

■ ■ ■

In situations like this, it is very important for carers to extend aspects of their care and to speak up for people with dementia if necessary, as they are not able to express their own feelings or wishes. Usually I am very friendly and understanding towards other healthcare professionals as I used to be a nurse myself, but looking back, I realise I behaved like a mother lion protecting her cub from threatening predators on the day Sylvia was admitted.

I had just got Sylvia settled for the night in the room she had been allocated earlier that afternoon when a nurse informed us that Sylvia needed to be moved to a different room. I immediately acted as her advocate and insisted on talking to the nurse in the corridor outside, explaining firmly and clearly exactly why the move was not going to happen.

I could not have cared less when, a few minutes later, I saw a group of nurses gathered round the nursing station whispering and giving me the sort of look that is reserved for a troublemaker. However, they did not move her anywhere that night. My mission had been completed. Linda took over for the night and Sylvia stayed where she was.

I arrived back at the hospital at eight o'clock the following morning and greeted the morning staff on the ward before going into Sylvia's room. Soon afterwards, there was a knock on the door and a nurse asked me if she could talk to me for a second. 'Here we go,' I thought and I was prepared for the worst as I slowly walked out into the corridor.

'I just thought I must say this. What you did last night was really remarkable and I hope I have someone like you on my side when I get dementia,' she said quietly and confidentially, smiled at me and walked away.

I do not know exactly how long I stood there alone outside Sylvia's door, but the feeling of pleasure and pride I experienced as I went back into Sylvia's room and saw her content and comfortable in her hospital bed is something I will always remember. Receiving valuable feedback and reassurance when you do get things right is priceless.

■ ■ ■

A couple of months after Sylvia's hospital stay it was Christmas. Despite her recurring health problems, Sylvia was in good spirits.

Sylvia is sitting in her favourite spot on the sofa enjoying a Christmas Eve classical concert full of familiar festive tunes on TV. I can see her out of the corner of my eye busily hiding fragments of a chocolate biscuit that she has carefully broken into tiny pieces under everything within reach. One is being secreted behind a cushion, another under her napkin on the arm of the sofa, one is finding its way into her Colin Dexter book on the small table in front of her.

Suddenly she is distracted for a moment, enjoying the music and beating in time with Sleigh Ride, *then she is back again to her very important task, and looks under the napkin on her right. The chocolate biscuit is still there. She looks for somewhere else to hide the remaining crumbs.*

I do not distract or stop her. She is so relaxed, happy and comfortable, and she has not realised that for the very first time in her entire life, she is not spending Christmas with her daughter. Linda and her husband have gone away for a much-needed short break after a very tiring, eventful and busy year.

I had no idea that that would be the last Christmas we would spend together.

■ ■ ■

The palliative care state in Sylvia's final illness only lasted four weeks. It started in the middle of the night after New Year's Day when she suddenly called out. She could not describe exactly what was happening to her. All she could say was, 'Please get this out of my head! Smack me or something. Please help me.' There was nothing to indicate that she was having a stroke. All her vital signs were within normal range and she insisted she was not in any pain, as people living with dementia usually do. After contacting Linda and the agency I work for to report what had happened, I stayed with her and held her hand until she settled and eventually fell asleep.

Over the next couple of days her mobility decreased dramatically and just three mornings after that initial episode she was not able to stand up and could not support herself by holding onto the rail in the bathroom. The wheelchair that had been kept stored away 'just in case' or for long walks that would have been too tiring suddenly became a crucial piece of equipment, and I used it to move her from one room to another on those few occasions when there was a temporary improvement in her condition during her last month. Her loss of appetite, her lack of interest in most things around her, her failing voice, her constant tiredness and her weak pulse were all signs that the end was not far away.

It was Sylvia's choice to ask for a priest and her request provided a further definite sign that she was ready to leave this world as she had never practised any religion. During her last fortnight she talked about the Lord a lot, she insisted on having the rosary around her neck and grabbed hold of the cross as it was the only thing on earth that could save her from anything unpleasant ahead, and she kept asking for an invisible light to be put out. Gradually her murmuring speech became slurred until even giving a 'Yes' or 'No' answer made her breathless and exhausted.

I knew she was dying and the last four years that we had spent together filled my mind. As Sylvia often said, we shared 'A jolly good time'. Of course there were ups and downs, but it was jolly, it was good and it is something that I will never forget. Her farewell was peaceful and quiet, it all happened in her sleep, in her own home, surrounded by her well-known and much-loved objects, and it was the voice of her old-time favourite, John McCormack, the Irish singer, that accompanied her to the other side.

I finish packing my suitcase and then say goodbye to Sylvia's family and friends. Ready to leave, I stop for a moment, and once more look back from the front door, staring at the chair in the kitchen where I first saw Sylvia sitting at the table, almost exactly four years ago.

Flashes of memories cross my mind in these few seconds: I

hear her singing a song, I see her reading her book, enjoying the view by the river with her lovely smile on her face, obsessively packing and unpacking her handbag, watering the cactuses, putting on her cherry-red lipstick, pushing the trolley at the supermarket, waiting at the doctor's surgery, enjoying her delicious chocolate cake at the marina and flirting with the handsome waiter at the café.

I gently pull the door to behind me. Turning my face into the sun, I put on my sunglasses. The breezy air swallows my sigh and by the time I get into the taxi, it is only a contented smile that can be seen on my face.

I have a train to catch. Not to mention Ivy and her dementia with Lewy bodies waiting for me.

■ ■ ■

NOTES AND BIBLIOGRAPHY

Chapter One: Tightrope walking on my nerves

1. (Page 15) Zeisel J (2009) *I'm Still Here: A Breakthrough Approach to Understanding Someone Living with Alzheimer's*. New York: Penguin Group (USA), New York.

Chapter Four: Who has been fired from the factory?

2. (Page 41) Alzheimer's Australia (Qld) (2008) *How the brain works – Introduction to dementia*. Issue No 2. Commonwealth Department of Human Services and Health September 1994, Dementia Care Learning Program

Chapter Six: Terrifying numbers

3. Alzheimer's Society (2015) Dementia 2014 report statistics https://www.alzheimers.org.uk/site/scripts/documents_info. php?documentID=341 (Accessed 3 August 2016)
4. Parkinson's UK (2016) Dementia and Parkinson's. http://www.parkinsons.org.uk/dementia (Accessed 3 August 2016)

Chapter Nine: The 'Must Not Do' list

5. (Page 100) Stokes G, Goudie F (2002) *The Essential Dementia Care Handbook: A Good Practice Guide*. London, UK: Speechmark Publishing.

Chapter Ten: There is always someone behind dementia

6. (Page 109) Validation Organization. Naomi Feil: Biography. https://vfvalidation.org/naomi-feil-bio/ (Accessed 3 August 2016)
7. (Page 109) Neal M, Briggs M (2003) Validation therapy for dementia. *The Cochrane Database of Systematic Reviews*, Issue 3, Art. No: CD001394. DOI:10.1002/14651858.C001394.
8. Gladys Wilson and Naomi Feil. https//www.youtube.com/watch?v=CrZXz10FcVM (Accessed 3 August 2016)
9. (Page 112) Webster JD (1993) Construction and validation of the Reminiscence Functions Scale. *Journals of Gerontology: Psychological Sciences* 48: 256–262.

Chapter Twelve: The Secret language

10. (Page 134) Abbey J, De Bellis A, Piller N et al. *The Abbey Pain Scale*. Funded by the JH and JD Medical Research Foundation 1998-2002. http://prc.coh.org/PainNOA/Abbey_Tool.pdf (Accessed 3 August 2016)
11. (Page 134) Cornell Scale for Depression in Dementia. (This is a screening tool and is not regarded as diagnostic) http://geropsychiatriceducation.vch.ca/docs/edu-downloads/depression/cornell_scale_depression.pdf (Accessed 3 August 2016)
12. (Page 135) CALD Intergenerational Dementia Project, Spectrum Migrant Resource Centre, Melbourne. Reported at the Hammond Care 8th Biennial International Conference on Dementia, Sydney 2010.

Chapter Thirteen: I've got bloody dementia!

13. (Page 146) Reisberg B, Auer SR, Montciro IM (1997) Behavioral Pathology in Alzheimer's Disease (BEHAVE-AD) Rating Scale. *International Psychogeriatrics* 8(S3) 301-308 For a useful summary see http://www.alzheimers.net/stages-of-alzheimers-disease/ (Accessed on 1 July 2016).

Chapter Sixteen: Self-assessment

14. (Page 190) Schrocr WJ (2008) Generations X, Y, Z, and the Others. WJSchroer Company. http://socialmarketing.org/archives/generation-x-y-z-and-the-others/ (Accessed 3 August 2016)

INDEX

*Note: Many of the themes listed in the index occur throughout the book. The page number(s) given in the Index refer to the place where they are a particular focus.